As-Suyuti's
Medicine of the Prophet
may Allah bless him and grant him peace

by

Jalalu'd-Din Abd'ur-Rahman As-Suyuti

Published by
Ta-Ha Publishers Ltd.

© Copyright Dhu'l-Hijjah 1414/June 1994 Ta-Ha Publishers

Reprinted: 1996, 1997, 1999, 2004, 2009

Published by:
Ta-Ha Publishers Ltd.
Unit 4, The Windsor Centre
Windsor Grove
West Norwood
LONDON SE27 9NT
website:http://www.taha.co.uk/
email: sales@taha.co.uk

Translated from *Tibb an-Nabbi*
by Jalalu'd-Din Abd'ur-Rahman As-Suyuti.

Edited and typeset by: Ahmad Thomson

Glossaries and Index compiled by Ahmad Thomson

British Library Cataloguing in Publication Data
As-Suyuti, Jalal'ud-Din Abd'ur-Rahman
As-Suyuti's Medicine of the Prophet
1. Islam
I. Title

ISBN 1 897940 15 7

Printed and Bound by - De-Luxe Printers,
London NW10 7NR

Contents

Part Three

About the Author

Jalalu'd-Din Abd'ur-Rahman ibn Abi Bakr as-Suyuti, who is generally known simply as as-Suyuti, was born in Asyut in Upper Egypt in 848 AH/1445 CE. His family originally came from Persia and he also had Turkish ancestry.

As-Suyuti had memorised the Qur'an by heart by the age of eight, and became a scholar of the Muslim sciences. During his life he wrote many books on a wide variety of subjects, of which *Tibb an-Nabbi* was one of the most popular. Indeed it can still be purchased in Arabic today.

There are several other important works concerning the medicine of the Prophet, may Allah bless him and grant him peace, most of which share the same title – *Tibb an-Nabbi* – and it is helpful not to confuse them. Perhaps two of the better known of these works are those compiled by Abu Nu'aim (died in 430 AH/1038 CE) who was from Persia, and Ibn al-Qayyim al-Jawziyya (died in 751 AH/ 1350 CE) who was from North Africa.

As-Suyuti, who died at the age of sixty, in 911 AH/1505 CE, clearly knew these earlier works well, for he refers to their authors several times in his book, as well as being familiar with more detailed works such as that of Ibn Sina, who was affectionately renamed 'Avicenna' by the Europeans.

It is clear from as-Suyuti's writing that his knowledge of medicine was not merely academic, but based on sound practice and experience, and it is equally clear from what he says that the art of medicine and the gift of healing are not merely the result of experimentation and good luck, but rather a divinely revealed science whose results are ultimately and essentially the outcome of the mercy and the decree of Allah:

And when I am sick, then He heals me.

(Qur'an: 26.80)

Acknowledgements

The publishers would like to thank Cyril Elgood, whose translation of As-Suyuti's work has been of great help in the preparation of this translation.

Author's Introduction

In the Name of Allah the Merciful the Compassionate

Praise belongs to Allah Who has given existence to every self, and Who has inspired each one towards right actions and wrong actions, and Who has taught what is good for them and what is harmful for them, what causes sickness and what gives health, and Who has created death and granted new life.

And I bear witness that there is no god except Allah, and that He is One and without a partner. And I bear witness that Muhammad is His Prophet and His slave. He has sent him with mercy for whoever is worthy of mercy, and with punishments for whoever deserves punishment. May the mercy of Allah be on him and his family for ever and ever until the Day of Rising and the Day of Good News.

To continue, it is obligatory on every Muslim to draw as close to Allah the Almighty as he can, and to expend all his energy in paying attention to His commands and being obedient to Him, and to make the best use of the means that he has, and to be successful in drawing near to Him by acting in accordance with what is commanded and avoiding what is forbidden, and to strive for whatever gives benefit to mankind by preserving good health and treating disease – for good health is essential in order to fulfil the obligations of the deen and to worship Allah.

Truly I have relied on Allah in my collecting some of the wise sayings of the Prophet, may Allah bless him and grant him peace, which are concerned with medicine. Whatever is required to preserve good health and whatever is inimical to good health, are all to be found here. I seek the help of Allah. My aim is His glory and His acceptance. He is my support, the most excellent of protectors. There is no power and no strength except from Allah, the Beloved, the Wise.

If you find any fault, then correct it, I pray,
for no one is faultless except Allah, you must say.

Part One

1

The Theory of Medicine

The Constitution of Man

The constitution of man is made up of seven constituents:

The **first** constituent is the Elements, which are four in number:

> Fire, which is hot and dry;
> Air, which is hot and wet;
> Water, which is cold and wet; and
> Earth, which is cold and dry.

The **second** constituent is the Temperaments, which are nine in number:

The first is an evenly balanced temperament.
The second is an unevenly balanced temperament, which may be unmixed, being then hot, cold, wet, or dry.
Or it may be an unevenly balanced but mixed temperament, being hot and dry, or hot and wet, or cold and dry, or cold and wet.
The most evenly balanced of all temperaments in the animal kingdom is the temperament of man. The most evenly balanced of all temperaments in mankind is the temperament of the believer. The most evenly balanced of all temperaments among the believers are the temperaments of the Prophets, peace be on them. The most evenly balanced of temperaments among all the Prophets are the temperaments of the Messengers of Allah, may the blessings and peace of Allah be on them. And the most evenly balanced of temperaments among all the Messengers of Allah is the temperament of those endowed with a resolution to obey Allah. And the most evenly balanced of those so endowed is the temperament of our master Muhammad, may Allah bless him and grant him peace.

I maintain that the reason why Muhammad, may Allah bless him and grant him peace, was the most evenly balanced in character from the point of view of temperament according to the rules of Medicine is because the nature of his character was subservient to the temperament of his body – and the more perfectly balanced the temperament of the body is, the better is the nature of the character. And He the all-Knowing, Glorious and Mighty is He, has born witness that the Prophet was of an excellent character:

And surely you are on a mighty nature.

(Qur'an: 68.4)

'Ayesha, may Allah be pleased with her, said, "The character of the Prophet, may Allah bless him and grant him peace, is the Qur'an." Hence it needs must be that his temperament be the most balanced of temperaments. And if his temperament were the most balanced of temperaments, then his character must have been the best of characters.

Al-Bukhari said in his book, as-Sahih, "The Prophet, may Allah bless him and grant him peace, was the best of men in appearance and the best of men in character."

Anas said, "I served the Prophet, may Allah bless him and grant him peace, for ten years. He never once scolded me. He never asked me why I had done anything that I had done, nor asked me why I had left undone anything that I had left undone."

Ibn 'Umar said, "The Prophet, may Allah bless him and grant him peace, was never indecent, nor ever talked indecently. He used to say, 'The best of you are those who are finest in character.'"

Al-Bukhari relates that a Bedouin once pulled a cloak from the shoulders of the Prophet, may Allah bless him and grant him peace, with so violent a pull that he hurt his shoulder. Then he said, "O Muhammad, make me a present from the wealth of Allah which you possess." The Prophet turned to him, laughed, and ordered a gift to be made to him.

Truly the Prophet, may Allah bless him and grant him peace, is good and chaste, the best of men in features and in character.

May Allah bless him and his followers with a blessing which will never end and never be exhausted:

The Merciful One has never created another like Muhammad,
and to my knowledge He never will create one like him:
he is like the sun at mid-day,
and the moon at mid-month;
he is the emerald among jewels;
his station is one that has never been given to other messengers;
his rank is one that has never been given to other men.

Now, the temperament of youth is evenly balanced. The temperament of childhood inclines to wetness, and that of maturity and old age to coldness.

The most evenly balanced of the organs is the skin of the tip of the index finger and after this the tips of the other fingers. The hottest of the organs is the heart, and after that the liver and the flesh. The coldest of all are the bones and the nerves, the spinal cord and the brain. The driest of all is bone. The wettest of all is fat.

Next among the seven constituents of the constitution, the **third**, come the four Humours:

Of these the most excellent is Blood, which is wet and hot. Its function is to feed the body. Normal blood is sweet and without smell.

Next comes Phlegm, and this is wet and cold. Its function is to convert blood whenever the body lacks food, to keep the organs moist and to prevent dehydration due to movement. Normal phlegm is phlegm that is near to changing into blood. Abnormal phlegm is salty, or somewhat warm, or sour. It tends to be ripe and insipid. It is unmixed cold.

The third humour is Bile, which is dry and hot. It is stored in the gall bladder. It renders the blood subtle and helps it tu pass through the very narrow veins. Part of it is carried to the bowels and produces the characteristic colour of the faeces. Normal bile is slightly red. Abnormal bile may be coloured like the yoke of an egg, or coloured like leeks or verdigris, or be inflamed. Rusty bile is more powerful than leek-coloured bile, and it is a warning of death. Bile is sometimes known as Yellow Bile.

Finally, there is Spleen. This is dry and cold. It thickens the blood and feeds the spleen and the bones. Part of it passes to the mouth of the stomach and sets up a desire for food and causes acidity. Normal spleen forms the dregs of the blood. Abnormal spleen is described as inflamed, that is, impure. Spleen is sometimes called Black Bile.

The **fourth** constituent of the constitution is the Fundamental Organs.

The **fifth** constituent is the Spirits.

The **sixth** constituent is the Faculties, and they are three in number: the Natural, the Vital, and the Psychic.

And the **seventh** and last constituent is the Functions, and they are two: the Function of Attraction and the Function of Repulsion.

The State of the Body

The second of the four areas into which the theory of medicine is divided is concerned with the theory of the state of the body of man.

There are three states of the body that are possible: health, disease, and a condition which is neither health nor disease, that is, convalescence and old age.

Now, health is a physical condition in which all the functions are healthy. Being restored to good health is the best gift of Allah to man. It is impossible to act rightly and to pay proper attention to the obedience which is due to our Lord except when health is present. There is nothing like it. Let the worshipper give thanks for his health and never be ungrateful.

The Prophet said, may Allah bless him and grant him peace, "There are two gifts of which many men are cheated – good health and leisure." Al-Bukhari transmitted this hadith.

The Prophet said, may Allah bless him and grant him peace, "There are worshippers of Allah whom He protects from death in battle and from sickness. He makes them live in good health and die in good health, and yet He grants them the stations of His martyrs."

Abu-d-Darda said, "O Prophet, if I am cured of my sickness and am thankful for it, is it better than if I were sick and bore it patiently?" And the Prophet, may Allah bless him and grant him peace, replied, "Truly the Prophet loves good health, just as you do."

It has been related that at-Tirmidhi said, "The Prophet, may Allah bless him and grant him peace, said, 'Whoever awakes in the morning with a healthy body, and a self that is sound, and whose provision is assured, he is like the one who possesses the whole world.'"

Again, at-Tirmidhi has related that Abu Huraira said that the Prophet, may Allah bless him and grant him peace, said, "The first question that is put to the worshipper on the Day of Rising about the pleasures of this world is: 'Did I not give you a healthy body?' And the next is: 'Did I not satisfy you with cool water?'"

And again, he has also related that the Prophet, may Allah bless him and grant him peace, said, "O 'Abbas, ask Allah for health in this world and in the next." Al-Bazar reports this hadith.

The Prophet, may Allah bless him and grant him peace, also said, "Ask Allah for forgiveness and health. After certainty of faith, nothing better is given to a man than good health." This has been transmitted by an-Nasa'i.

"No supplication is more pleasing to Allah than a request for good health," is a hadith related by at-Tirmidhi.

A certain bedouin once questioned the Prophet, may Allah bless him and grant him peace, saying, "O Prophet of Allah, what supplication shall I make to Allah after I have finished doing the prayer?" And he replied, "Ask for good health."

Among the wise sayings of the Prophet Daw'ud, peace be on him, are the following: "Health is a hidden kingdom." And again, "Sadness for one hour ages a man by one year." And again, "Health is a crown on the heads of the healthy that only the sick can see." And again, "Health is an invisible luxury."

Some of our ancestors used to say, "How many rich gifts Allah has placed beneath every vein."

And may Allah indeed give us health in the deen in this life and in the next.

As for disease, it is a state that is just the opposite of this. It arises from need, or from wrong action, or from misfortune.

The Causes of Disease

The third of the four areas into which the theory of medicine is divided deals with the theory of causes, or aetiology.

Now, there are six Causes:

The **first** of these is Air. Air is essential to keep the self evenly balanced, for as long as air remains pure, no debility is mixed within it, and no impure wind. It is an invisible protection.

Each season produces diseases compatible with it, and expels what is incompatible. Thus, summer causes bile and results in bilious diseases, but cures cold diseases. And the like can be said of the other seasons.

Cold air is strengthening and improves the digestion. Hot air has just the reverse effect. A change in the air is a cause of pestilence, and this will be described later, insh'Allah.

The **second** cause is Food and Drink. When hot, these produce heat in the body, and vice versa.

The **third** cause is Bodily Movement and Rest. Movement causes warmth in the body, and vice versa.

The **fourth** cause is Emotional Movement and Rest, as occurs in cases of anger, joy, anxiety, grief and shame. These states set the self in motion – certainly inwardly, but also outwardly apparent. I will return to these later, insh'Allah.

The **fifth** cause is Waking and Sleeping. Sleep makes the self bubble within the body, although it cools it outwardly, so the sleeper needs some outer covering. Wakefulness is just the opposite of this.

The **sixth** cause is Emission and Retention. A balance between these protects health.

Signs in a Man

The fourth of the four areas into which the theory of medicine is divided deals with the theory of signs.

Black hair and a black body are signs of heat – and the opposite a sign of cold. Similarly, with a fat body or a thin body. An excess of flesh is a sign of heat combined with wetness. An excess of fat is a sign of cold combined with wetness. In the same way, an excessive desire for sleep is a sign of wetness, whereas a diminished desire is a sign of dryness. A moderate desire is the sign of a balanced temperament.

Similarly, the appearance of the organs is a sign. Capacious organs are a sign of hotness, and the opposite a sign of coldness. In the same way, dreams indicate temperaments. Seeing colours like yellow or red, or flashes of light, all these are signs of hotness – and their opposites are signs of coldness. Again, excess of body odour is a sign of heat, and lack of it a sign of coldness.

2

The Practice of Medicine

Food

Know then that food is taken when required for the preservation of health. Signs of its being needed are an increase in the sense of smell, a deficiency of saliva in the mouth, highly coloured urine with a strong smell, and an increased desire for food. The opposite of these indicates that food is not required.

Going without food for a long time wearies the body, and dehydrates it, and burns up its constitution. Similarly, having food when it is not needed results in stupidity and laziness and is one of the factors that cause disease.

Al-Muwaffiq 'Abdal-Latif said, "It is the custom of the Indians when they want food, firstly to wash or put on a clean outer garment, and then to sprinkle a pleasant scent over themselves, and to remain quiet and abstain from sexual intercourse, and only then to concern themselves with their food."

Later, insh'Allah, there will be a chapter on what arises from this chapter.

A man should eat cold foods in summer, and hot ones in winter. Having one meal right after another is harmful. So is taking exercise after a meal – but exercise before a meal is best of all, just as when taken after, it is worst of all. Hot food should be balanced with cold, sweet with sour, fat with salt, and acid with fat. Having many kinds of food excites the constitution of a man. To eat with relish is best of all. Having the same food several times in a row and eating hurriedly produces a loss of appetite and causes laziness. Food that is very sour hurries on old age. Eating sweet food frequently diminishes sexual desires and makes the body feverish. Salty food dries up and emaciates the body.

It is wise to stop eating while you still have an appetite for more, but persistent abstention makes the body grow weak and thin. Indeed, abstaining from food when healthy is the same as mixing many different foods when unwell. Always choose the best food, unless a bad habit has been formed – in which case it should be given up gradually. Whoever is used to eating the wrong food should not stop it altogether, but should avoid taking food that will ferment in the stomach, such as over-ripe fruit.

Wiping the dish clean helps the digestion and increases sexual desires. The Prophet, may Allah bless him and grant him peace, used to lick his fingers three times after meals. He used to say, "Wiping the dish clean is a request for forgiveness."

The Prophet, may Allah bless him and grant him peace, forbade eating the following together at the same meal: milk and fish, or vinegar and milk, or fruit and milk, or lettuce and fish, or garlic and onions, or dried meat and fresh meat, or sour things and acid things, or sumach and vinegar, or vinegar and rice, or grapes and excessive eating of aubergines, or pomegranates and meat pudding, or two cold dishes, or two hot dishes, or two wind-producing dishes.

It is wise to avoid vinegar and fat if the container is made of copper; and similarly, cheese and roast meats and hot food if wrapped in bread or anything like it. This is one of the reasons for the prohibition of eating anything found dead.

Again, one should avoid uncovered food or uncovered water, in case something poisonous has fallen into it that might be fatal if one were to eat or drink it. The Prophet, may Allah bless him and grant him peace, commanded this when he said, "Cover over your containers and stop up the mouths of your water bottles, for truly there is a night in the year in which a pestilence comes down and does not settle on any uncovered container without falling into it." Indeed all physicians are in agreement with this command of the Prophet. The reference to the heavens has been related by Muslim.

Whoever eats onions for forty days will get freckles on his face. There is no one to blame but yourself if this happens. Whoever of you has an average build and eats salt will be afflicted with leucoderma and scabies. And for this blame no one but your self. Whoever eats fish and eggs together will become paralysed, and for this blame no one but yourself. Whoever has a wet dream and does not wash before having sexual intercourse will produce an idiot or an epileptic. And for this blame no one but yourself. Whoever eats until he is full and then gets into a hot bath will become paralysed, and for this blame no one but your self. Whoever gazes into a mirror at night will become afflicted with facial paralysis. And for this blame no one but your self.

It has been related by Anas that the Prophet, may Allah bless him and grant him peace, said, "The root of every disease is coldness." And again, it has been reported by Ibn Mas'ud that he said, "Cold means a bloody flux, for this cools even the heat of sexual desire."

It is essential that a man restrains himself to eating what is suitable and appetising, but without excess. The Prophet, may Allah bless him and grant him peace, said, "The Tribe of Adam fill no container worse than the way in which they fill their own stomachs. Let the Tribe of Adam just have a few mouthfuls to strengthen the loins. If possible, one third of the stomach is for food, one third for drink, and one third for one's breath." This hadith is reported by an-Nasa'i and at-Tirmidhi, and it is a good and reliable hadith.

The following section consists of some further observations concerning health:

'Ali ibn al-Husayn ibn Wafid said, "Allah put all medicine into half an ayah when He said:

Eat and drink, but not excessively.

(Qur'an: 7.31)

'Umar, may Allah be pleased with him, said, "Avoid having a pot-belly, for it spoils the body, causes disease, and makes doing the prayer tiring. Make use of blood letting, for this puts the body right. And avoid all excess, for Allah hates a learned man who is fat." This is reported by Abu Nu'aim.

Hippocrates said, "The maintenance of good health depends on working in moderation and avoiding eating and drinking too much." He also said, "A little of what is harmful is better than a lot of what is good."

Al-Shahrastani said in his book called *Al-Milal wa'n-Nihal*, or *The Book of Religions and Sects*, "Hippocrates is the founder of Medicine." And he added, "Our ancestors and those who came later prefer him above all others. A certain Greek king sent him several qintars of gold and asked him to come and visit him. But he refused. He also used to refuse any fee for treating the poor or people of average means – but he stipulated that from the rich he would take one of three things: a necklace of gold, or a diadem, or golden bracelets."

When asked what life is best, Hippocrates replied, "Safety with poverty is better than wealth with fear." He also said, "Everyone should be treated with herbs from his own country." When he was dying he said, "You can recognise the one who seeks knowledge by his sleeping a great deal, his mild nature, his soft skin, and his long life."

He also said, "If man had been created with only one constitution, he would never have suffered illness – for then there would have been no opposites to cause disease."

A physician once visited a sick man and said to him, "You, the disease and I are three. If by listening to me you help me, then we shall be two against one and accordingly stronger – and when two come up against one, they defeat it."

Hippocrates was once asked, "Why does a man weigh more when he is dead than when he was alive?" He replied, "Before he was made up out of two parts, a light part lifting him up and a heavy part weighing him down. When one of these departed – and it was the light part that does the lifting that went – then the heavy part weighs him down even more."

He once said to one of his students, "Let your best means of treating people be your love for them, your taking an interest in their affairs, your understanding of their condition, and your clearly paying attention to them."

He also said, "All excess is contrary to the laws of Nature. Let your eating, your drinking, your sleeping, and your sexual intercourse, all be in moderation."

And he said, "Any physician who administers a poison, or procures an abortion, or prevents a pregnancy, or prolongs the disease of a sick man – such a physician is no colleague of mine. On this subject he formulated a well-known oath which I shall discuss later, insh'Allah.

The books on medicine by Hippocrates are many. Among them are: *The Book of Aphorisms*, *The Book of Prognoses*, and the *Kitab Qubra Buqrat*, or *The Book of Opened Graves*. This last book testifies to many wonderful wonders. When the tombs of several of the Greek kings were opened, this book was found inside them.

Harith ibn Kalada, the physician of the Arabs was once asked, "What is the best medicine?" He replied, "Necessity – that is, hunger." When he was asked, "What is disease?", he replied, "The entry of food upon food."

Ibn Sina said, "Never have a meal until the one before it has been digested."

Hot food is to be avoided. The Prophet, may Allah bless him and grant him peace, also disapproved of it. He also forbade eating while lying down. This has been related by al-Bukhari. Abu ibn Ka'b explained that this is because it was the custom of tyrants.

It was not the practice of the Prophet, may Allah bless him and grant him peace, to blow on his food or his drink, or to breathe into a container.

Walking after dinner is beneficial, or doing the prayer has the same effect, for then the food sits in the pit of the stomach and the digestion is better.

It has been related that the Prophet, may Allah bless him and grant him peace, said, "Digest your food with the Name of Allah and with a prayer. And do not go to sleep immediately after eating, for this will make you constipated." This hadith has been transmitted by Abu Nu'aim.

And do not take vigorous exercise after eating, for this is harmful. Never go without your supper, for this makes a man grow old. Anas reported the following well-known hadith: "Eat some supper, even if it is only a handful of dry bread, for going without the evening meal makes you grow old." This was transmitted by at-Tirmidhi. Similarly, Jabir is reported to have said, "Never go without supper, even if it is only a handful of dates, for going without it ages a man." This was transmitted by Ibn Maja.

The hands should be washed clean of the smell of food. The Prophet, may Allah bless him and grant him peace, used to say, "The believer puts food into one stomach, the unbeliever into seven." Wisdom will not enter a stomach stuffed with food. The less a man eats, the less he drinks; and the less he drinks, the less he sleeps; and the less he sleeps, the more blessed will be his old age. The more a man eats, the more he drinks; and the more a man drinks, the heavier will he sleep; and whoever sleeps heavily, loses the blessings of old age. If a man is satisfied before he is full, then the better will his body be nourished, and the better will be the state of his self and his heart – but as for the man who is full up with food, his body will be badly nourished, his self will be in a bad state, and his heart will grow hard. So avoid too much food, for it poisons the heart, slows down the limbs of the body in the obedience that is due to Allah, and closes the ears to His commands.

Plato said, "Whoever goes out into the open before going to sleep will certainly retain the beauty of his complexion." Indeed the Prophet, may Allah bless him and grant him peace, commanded this, according to the hadith transmitted by al-Barr ibn 'Azib, when he said, "Before you go to sleep, do wudu just as you do before doing the prayer." This is a sound and reliable hadith.

Drink

Never drink water immediately after having eaten, nor when the stomach is completely empty. Whoever drinks water from a well will have his food well digested. Avoid drinking very cold water, for it is harmful to the respiratory organs, especially after a hot meal, or after sweet food, or after a hot bath, or after sexual intercourse. Do not mix well-water with river-water.

Never swallow water with a single gulp, for a disease called al-Kabar is caused by drinking in this way. Al-Bayhaqi explains that 'al-Kabar' means 'pain in the liver', and that 'a single gulp' means 'swallowing in great gulps'. Anas has transmitted the hadith that the Prophet, may Allah bless him and grant him peace, used to take three breaths, one after each sip, and used to say that because of this it was more satisfying, healthier, and more thirst-quenching. Anas added, "I also used to take three breaths in the same way." Muslim transmitted this hadith.

Abu Nu'aim has also transmitted the hadith that whenever the Prophet, may Allah bless him and grant him peace, had a drink (sharab), he would pause three times to take a breath, invoking the Name of Allah when he began and praising Him when he paused. The word 'sharab' means 'water' in this context, although in the terminology of physicians it means 'intoxicant'.

According to at-Tirmidhi, the Prophet, may Allah bless him and grant him peace, used to use the toothpick from the side, and would drink by sucking in.

The meaning of the phrase 'take a breath' in the ahadith is drinking with three pauses for breath by removing the mouth from the container.

The prohibition by the Prophet, may Allah bless him and grant him peace, against breathing into a container means that it is forbidden to drink from and breathe into a container without removing the container from the mouth – for sometimes some saliva may drop into the container, and if this happens often enough the container may become contaminated. Thus there is no contradiction between what he has ordered and what he has forbidden.

It is certainly very beneficial to ration one's water. This is because some need may make it seem necessary to drink a lot of water, because of extreme thirst – and yet a man cannot be sure of having repeated opportunities to have a drink and reduce his temperature. Rationing one's water makes this more certain.

The benefit of pausing for breath while drinking is as follows: Breathing stops at the moment of swallowing – and yet there is a great need both for water and for breath. And if a man takes a breath and inhales a drop of water into the respiratory passage, then it will make him cough or choke. But if a man pauses while drinking to take a breath, then he will be safe from this.

And as for the statement about taking three breaths, certainly there is no need for more than this, but it is advisable for everyone to take three breaths when drinking, just as the Prophet did, may Allah bless him and grant him peace.

As regards the statement that this is more satisfying, it certainly is more satisfying for the thirst than drinking everything all in one gulp.

As for it being healthier, this is because if a man is having a drink for this reason, he will be cured of his disease completely, or he will recover from his disease more swiftly.

As for it being more thirst-quenching or more penetrating, this is because it helps the digestion and encourages the appetite.

These are fine points of wisdom and hidden truths, which are not always pointed out, except by those who are meticulous. The wise of the earlier times and of the later times were unable to grasp them – and may the blessings and peace of Allah be on this Prophet, the Physician, the Pure One, and may His mercy last for ever without end.

Anas said, "The Prophet, may Allah bless him and grant him peace, forbade drinking while standing up." But al-Khattabi said, "This prohibition refers to quenching thirst and to giving it a limit." Al-Khattabi allowed a drink to be taken while standing, as also did 'Umar, 'Uthman, 'Ali, may Allah be pleased with them, and many of the 'ulama'. Others refused. The Prophet himself, may Allah bless him and grant him peace, drank standing up.

The Prophet, may Allah bless him and grant him peace, forbade the kinking of water skins – that is he forbade the practice of kinking the neck of a waterskin and then drinking from the 'cup' that was thus formed. This has been reported by al-Bukhari. The reason for this prohibition is that it is because the drinker will not know what is going into his mouth – for there might be a leech in the water, or something else that might stick in his throat. Such things have been known.

Ibn Maja says, on the authority of Ibn Abbas, that the Prophet, may Allah bless him and grant him peace, possessed a cup and a flask and used to drink out of these.

Al-Muwaqqaf Abdal-Latif said, "Glass is best for a drinking vessel. The Indians preferred it. Their kings used to drink from glass and preferred it to silver and rubies, for it is less likely to carry dirt and becomes like new again when washed. Water that is dirty, or any drink that is dirty, can be detected through it – and it is difficult for a cup-bearer to put poison into it. These are its most excellent characteristics, for which the kings of India chose it."

Movement and Rest

Know then that moderate exercise is a most efficacious means of preserving good health. It warms the organs, and dissolves waste products, and makes the body light and active. The best time for it is after food has left the stomach, which it takes about five or six hours to do – more or less, depending on the constitution of the individual and of the food. By 'moderate exercise' is meant exercise which makes the skin red and glow. When sweating begins, then that is the right time to stop. Whatever increases sweating is called 'heavy exercise'.

Every organ is strengthened and enlivened by regular exercise. The same is true of the inner faculties. Whoever wishes to improve his memory will improve it by memorising. The same applies to the intellect and to thought. So, for every organ there is a specific exercise. Thus for the chest there is talking, beginning with whispering, and then passing on to shouting. For the eyes there are small letters. And for the hearing there are soft, pleasing sounds.

Horse-riding provides moderate exercise for the whole body.

The Prophet, may Allah bless him and grant him peace, indicated a form of exercise to us which is good for our bodies and our hearts, when he said, "Raid – and you will become rich. Travel – and you will grow healthy." And again, he said, "Fasting brings health." His saying, "Digest your food with right actions and prayer," has already been quoted.

Sleeping

The best time to go to sleep is after food has been digested. It is wise to start off sleeping on the right side, just as the Prophet, may Allah bless him and grant him peace, used to do. This was confirmed by 'Ayesha when she said, "He, may Allah bless him and grant him peace, used to go to sleep starting on his right side, and facing Makka.

Sleep during the day is bad. It affects the complexion, gives rise to diseases, and makes a man lazy. It should be avoided, except during the mid-day heat, in accordance with the hadith of the Prophet, may Allah bless him and grant him peace, "Have some sleep, for the shayatin never sleep." And again, he said, "Make it easier for you to rise for prayer during the night by having a short sleep during the day." He also said, "Sleeping during the morning hinders provision."

It has been related by Jabir that the Prophet, may Allah bless him and grant him peace, forbade a man to sleep partly in the sun and partly in the shade. Among the ahadith it is also related that he forbade a man to sit partly in the sun and partly in the shade. These are the statements of al-Hafiz Abu Nu'aim. Abu Daw'ud has related the same in his book called *As-Sunan*.

'Ayesha, may Allah be pleased with her, said, "Whoever goes to sleep during the late afternoon will make himself go mad – and he only has himself to blame." Al-Imam said, "There is one thing that is forbidden for a man, and that is to sleep during the late afternoon, lest he lose his wits." Sleep is also forbidden after the dawn prayer until the sun has risen, and before the night prayer. The Prophet, may Allah bless him and grant him peace, disliked sleep before these two times as much as he disliked talking after them, although if such talk was about wisdom, or about Allah, or farming, then it was not disliked by him.

Sleeping face down is also forbidden, because such sleep is the sleep of the Fire.

Finally, it is better to go to sleep in wudu, as has already been stated in the hadith concerning purity.

Excretion

Nature must be softened as regards what she retains by using such foods as a decoction of safflower and raisins. Among the laxatives which soften nature as regards what she retains are dried roses, Syrian cucumber, Makkan senna, and tamarinds. These should be boiled in the honey of wild bees. All of these are well tried.

Emission through Sexual Intercourse

Jabir has transmitted a hadith of the Prophet, may Allah bless him and grant him peace, which says, "Go and take a virgin as your wife whom you will caress and who will caress you." Jabir said, "The Prophet, may Allah bless him and grant him peace, forbade the act of love before caressing."

Marriage is one of the practices of the messengers of Allah, may Allah bless them and grant them peace.

It is best to have sexual intercourse only after digestion is completed and when the body is in balance and in a normal condition, midway between hot and cold, and between being full and being empty – but if a man has to make a mistake, then intercourse on a full stomach is less harmful than repressing it. It is said that Ibn 'Umar never had intercourse except after a meal.

Intercourse should be avoided when one is tired, or sad, or disappointed, and also after taking medicine. It should only be indulged in when there is a strong desire, and only when this desire is aroused neither by effort nor by erotic ideas or sights. It should be the result of there being an excess of semen.

If intercourse does not exceed the bounds of moderation, then it revives inward energy, makes a man joyful, awakes his appetite for food, and dissipates sad thoughts, melancholy preoccupations and depression. Sexual abstinence has resulted in disease more than once. Intercourse safeguards health, but excessive intercourse results in tremors and palsies, and weakens the faculties, and dims the eyesight.

The Prophet, may Allah bless him and grant him peace, said, "Whoever among you is troubled by his sexual urge, let him marry – for marriage causes the eyes to be lowered and safeguards the private parts." This is a sound hadith and has been transmitted by al-Bukhari.

Do not have intercourse with an old woman, with a very young girl, or with a woman who is menstruating:

And if they ask you about menstruation, say:
'It is an illness, so let women alone during menstruation,
and do not go near them until they are cleansed;
and when they have purified themselves,
then go into them as Allah has commanded you.
Surely Allah loves those who turn to Him,
and He loves those who purify themselves.

(Qur'an: 2.222)

For that blood is decaying blood, and can harm the sexual organ of a man, causing ulceration. Indeed, I have seen this myself.

The Prophet, may Allah bless him and grant him peace, said, "Do anything rather than commit adultery. And whoever has intercourse with a menstruating woman should make compensation of one dinar, or half a dinar." – Although some say that he only needs to ask for Allah's forgiveness for his error.

The reasoning underlying this hadith is that a Jew, when his wife is menstruating, abstains from all intercourse with her, sets her apart in the house, and makes her eat and drink alone. When the Prophet learned of this, may Allah bless him and grant him peace, he said, "Except as regards intercourse, do everything differently to the Jews, for the curse of Allah and His anger is on them."

Never have intercourse with a woman who has had no sexual relations for a long time, nor with a woman who is sick, nor with one whose appearance is not pleasing to you. To lie with one who is beloved makes the heart rejoice.

A man once went and complained to the Prophet, may Allah bless him and grant him peace, that he had very few children. The Prophet told him to eat eggs. According to Abu Huraira, the Prophet once complained to the angel Jibril that he could not have sexual intercourse often enough. "What?" replied the angel, "Why do you not eat harisa? There is the strength of forty men in this dish!"

From Abu Rafi' comes this hadith: "I was seated once in the house of the Prophet, may Allah bless him and grant him peace. He passed his hand over his head and said, 'Make use of henna, the best of all dyes, for henna strengthens the skin and increases sexual energy.'" Anas, too, said, "Dye yourself with henna, for surely henna is rejuvenating, and makes a man handsome, and compels him to sexual intercourse."

Among the ahadith is the one that shaving the pubic hair stimulates intercourse. Abu Nu'aim has transmitted this hadith.

Among the foods that are excellent for this purpose are peas, onions, meat, eggs, cocks and sparrows. After these a man should drink fresh milk and then rest and say his prayers. Similarly, he should eat pine kernels, haricot beans, turnips, carrots, grapes, asparagus, and pistachio nuts, hazel nuts and their like. He should avoid acidic and salty foods. I will return to this subject in the section on Simple Remedies, insh'Allah.

Muslim has transmitted the hadith from Abu Sa'id that the Prophet, may Allah bless him and grant him peace, said, "If one of you has gone into his wife, and desires to approach her again, then he should first do wudu, and then have intercourse again." The Prophet also said, "If one of you has gone into his wife and has said, 'In the Name of Allah, keep shaytan away from us, and keep shaytan away from what You grant us,' then the child that is destined to come from them will never be troubled by shaytan."

Al-Bukhari has transmitted the hadith that a man should not go to sleep until he has done wudu, as was commanded by the Prophet, may Allah bless him and grant him peace, according to the hadith of 'Ayesha and others. The Prophet was meticulous in his sexual relations, and he ordered his example to be followed. He once said, "What I love in your world are women, and scent, and the coolness of my eye is in the prayer." An-Nasa'i has related the hadith that he said, "Scent is the food of the soul, and the soul is the riding beast of the faculties of man." Nothing is more helpful than scent after sexual intercourse.

When he, may Allah bless him and grant him peace, spoke of the prayer after the enjoyment of these two pleasures, he indicated that having sexual intercourse dispels the distraction of erotic urges and sexual desires – which destroy clarity of perception and concentration by interfering with the flow of reflection and thought, and by diminishing awareness of the deen. It is for this reason that physicians have described the sex drive as being a madness. And by Allah, it is the most common of manias, for it is the most irrepressible of all the things that can dominate man.

The Prophet, may Allah bless him and grant him peace, said, "I have never seen anything more capable of weakening a man's senses and his deen and of destroying his judgement than one of you women." Truly, a man's judgement is wiped out by the intensity of his lust and things like it. Accordingly it is necessary for the slave of Allah to strive for pure intentions – without which no prayer has any merit. The discussions of the 'ulama', along with the many ahadith concerning the self and evil whisperings, are well known: the Prophet, may Allah bless him and grant him peace, clearly expressed the requirement concerning the obligation of doing the prayer – and he emphasised it by referring to the sayings of other messengers of Allah and others – that the slave of Allah must at the time of the prayer have a heart that is free from vain thoughts and evil inclinations.

And after sexual intercourse a ghusl is obligatory.

And Allah knows best.

Physicians have said that causing seminal emission by hand causes distress and weakens the sexual appetite and erections of the penis. As well as this it is forbidden by the shari'ah.

Blood Letting and Cupping

Al-Bukhari has written on this subject in his chapter on Cupping. The Prophet, may Allah bless him and grant him peace, commanded cupping to be used, and said, "There are no remedies comparable to cupping and blood letting." This hadith was preserved by al-Bukhari.

It is said that there was once a man who complained to the Prophet, may Allah bless him and grant him peace, about a pain in the head. All that he said in reply was, "Get cupped." Nor will there be pain in the feet if they are stained with henna. This is a hadith related by Abu Daw'ud. And many are the ahadith on the benefits of cupping.

Among the accounts concerning letting blood from the veins, there are many which cannot be denied. The Prophet, may Allah bless him and grant him peace, told Abu ibn Ka'b, the physician, to puncture his skin and bleed him from a vein. Among the ahadith are these two: "The best medicine is cupping." And: "Cupping purifies the outside of the body, and bleeding from a vein purifies its inside."

Cupping is used in hot countries and blood letting in cold ones. It is essential to refrain from cupping when taking a hot bath, except when the blood is very thick – in which case it is good to have a hot bath and then be cupped one hour later. A full stomach is also to be avoided. The Prophet, may Allah bless him and grant him peace, said, "Cupping on an empty stomach is a medicine, and on a full stomach it is a disease."

Ibn Maja says that he heard Ibn Umar say, "Benefit is to be found in looking after the blood, so call for a friendly bleeder for me – and let him be neither too old nor too young – for I myself heard the Prophet, may Allah bless him and grant him peace, say, "Cupping on an empty stomach is best, for in it there is healing," – but in not doing it at all, there is even more safety and wisdom.

Cupping beneath the chin relieves pain in the teeth and face. Cupping on the legs is good for boils on the thighs and for gout and piles and irritation in the back. The benefits of cupping are even more than I have stated, even twice as much – but applying a cup over a boney nodule ruins the memory.

It is the clear opinion of Ahmad that charging a fee for cupping is disliked. Ibn Abbas said, "I cupped the Prophet, may Allah bless him and grant him peace, and he paid me a fee." Now, if the Prophet knew that this was bad, he would not have given it. This hadith is taken from al-Bukhari.

As regards the places for cupping, al-Bukhari states that Ibn Abbas said, "I cupped the Prophet, may Allah bless him and grant him peace, for a pain in the head." In another hadith he says that it was for a migraine, but Anas says, "The Prophet was cupped 'fi'l-akhazayn wa'l-kahal'." At-Tirmidhi has also transmitted this hadith. Now, the word 'al-akhazayn' means 'the sides of the neck' and 'al-kahal' means 'above the top of the neck'. Abu Huraira says that Abu Hind cupped the Prophet on the top of the head. Abu Daw'ud also says this. Anas says he was cupped on the top of the foot, and so also say at-Tirmidhi and an-Nasa'i.

As regards the days on which cupping is preferable, Abu Huraira said, "The Prophet, may Allah bless him and grant him peace, said, 'Whoever is cupped on the 17th, 19th, or 21st, day of the month will be cured of every disease.'" This has been related by Abu Daw'ud. As for his saying, 'cured of every disease', the reason for this is the paramount importance of blood. At-Tirmidhi has transmitted almost exactly the same hadith on the authority of Anas.

Abu Bakr, may Allah be pleased with him, used to forbid his family from being cupped on a Tuesday, and gave the Prophet, may Allah bless him and grant him peace, as his authority. He added, "On that day the blood does not clot easily."

However I maintain that this prohibition is all very well for cupping in times of health, but if a man is ill or in great need, then one should not bother about whether the date is the 17th or the 20th.

Al-Jallal said, "'Ismad ibn 'Asim told me that Hanbal had told them that Ahmad ibn Hanbal used to apply cups whenever the blood was turgid and at any time." This is what he said. And al-Bukhari said that Abu Musa was cupped at night.

Cupping originated in Isfahan.

Physicians say that cupping should be done when the moon is waning, and blood letting when the moon is waxing.

Know that if blood letting is done in the wrong place, or when it is not needed, then it weakens the faculties, and it removes both healthy humours as well as harmful ones. Blood letting and cupping should be avoided by whoever is suffering from enteritis, by whoever is convalescing, by whoever is very old, by whoever has a weak liver or stomach, by whoever suffers from palsy of the face or feet, and by women who are pregnant, or who have just given birth, or who are menstruating.

The best times for blood letting and cupping are on a Monday at any time, or on a Tuesday during the daytime, according to the season. Spring is the best season for blood letting, for purging by vomiting, for calming down morbid fears, and for much sexual activity. Summer is the time for cold foods which destroy bile, for restricting sexual intercourse, for avoiding loss of blood, and for increasing hot baths. A man should meet winter by wearing extra clothes and having strong, thick foods, such as tharid broth. The ahadith are plentiful in praise of these things. All of this has been related by al-Bukhari.

The Prophet, may Allah bless him and grant him peace, said, "Truly 'Ayesha excels other women just as tharid broth excels other foods." See that it contains a lot of meat.

Truly a man should desire a copious flow and emission of blood and phlegm, and in winter he should increase his exercise and his sexual activity.

The Emotions

The body is certainly affected by emotion. The emotions include anger, joy, anxiety, sorrow, and shame.

As regards anger, it heats up the body and dries it up. Anger was forbidden by the Prophet, may Allah bless him and grant him peace. It has been related by al-Bukhari that a man once said to the Prophet, "Please, give me some advice." And he replied, "Never be angry." The meaning of this hadith is that a man should never act out of anger. A proof of this is another saying of the Prophet, "Do not think as one of you does in a fit of anger." And we said, "Is there any man who does not suffer from fits of anger?" And he replied, "No, there is not, but there are men who master themselves when they are angry, and if they are bad-tempered they control themselves so that anger will not overcome them and make them act under its influence." And this is the meaning of the saying of the Almighty:

Those who restrain their anger.

(Qur'an: 3.134)

This confirms the existence of their anger and praises them for their restraint.

When the Prophet, may Allah bless him and grant him peace, was angry, it was evident in his face. He once said, "Anger is from shaytan, and shaytan is indeed created from fire, and fire is put out by water – so if any of you becomes angry, then he should do wudu." Abu Daw'ud has related this.

In the ahadith related by at-Tirmidhi appears the statement that anger is surely carried in the hearts of men. And which of you has not seen the reddening of the eyes and the swelling of the jugular veins?

Again, among the ahadith is this one: "Truly I know of a sentence which, if a man says it, will make his anger depart: 'I seek refuge in Allah from shaytan the outcast.'" This hadith has also been transmitted by Muslim.

Now, as for joy, its characteristic is to strengthen inward energy. If it is excessive, it may kill a man by making his soul depart. It has been said about more than one person that so-and-so died out of excess joy. Indeed such excess has been prohibited by the word of the Almighty:

Surely Allah does not love those who exult.

(Qur'an: 28.76)

However the joyfulness of the believers is permitted and is pleasing, as the Almighty says:

> **Rejoicing in what Allah has given them**
> **from His outpouring generosity.**

(Qur'an: 3.170)

And also:

> **Say: 'In the outpouring generosity of Allah,**
> **and in His mercy – in that let them rejoice.'**

(Qur'an: 10.58)

But as for anxiety and sorrow, these are the root of restless fevers. The Prophet, may Allah bless him and grant him peace, used to seek refuge in Allah from anxiety and sorrow. The ahadith say that whoever suffers from these a lot, his body grows ill. This has been related by Abu Nu'aim.

Please note the difference between anxiety and sorrow. The former involves something that is expected to come or to go, while the latter relates to something that has already happened or to something that is already over.

The Prophet, may Allah bless him and grant him peace, used to see refuge in Allah at the end of every prayer in order to escape anxiety and sorrow.

According to one hadith, Ibn Abbas said, "Whoever suffers a lot from cares and affliction should say frequently, 'There is no power and no strength except from Allah the High, the Mighty.'"

As for grief, it is associated with a present state of affairs. So a man who suffers a lot from grief should busy himself with what makes him forget himself. Thus it is said of the Prophet, may Allah bless him and grant him peace, that he said, "If affliction weighs down on any one of you, then let him take up his bow!"

At-Tirmidhi has transmitted the following hadith from Abu Huraira: Whenever anything worried him, the Prophet, may Allah bless him and grant him peace, would raise his head to heaven and say, "Glory be to Allah, the Great."

And there is the following hadith about 'Abdullah ibn Mas'ud: He used to say, "No worshipper who is afflicted with care and grief and who says, 'O Allah, I am your worshipper, with a father and mother who worshipped you. Everything that I have is in Your hands. Your wisdom is sure and Your decrees are just. I ask You by every Name by which You describe Yourself, or that You have sent down in Your Pure Book, or that you have revealed to any one of Your Creation, or that You have preferred to keep a secret known only to You, I ask You that You make the Qur'an the spring of my heart, the light of my breast, the banisher of my grief, and the remover of my care,' – no one who says this will do so without Allah driving away his grief and care, and replacing them with joy instead." This has been related by Ahmad in his *al-Musnad*, and by Ibn Hibban in his *as-Sahih*.

As regards shame, this is the emotion that is experienced when a man is ashamed of himself.

Habits

Physicians have said that a habit is second nature. Anas said, "The Prophet, may Allah bless him and grant him peace, used to eat after the night prayer." Abu Nu'aim has also transmitted this. 'Ayesha has related that he once came into her while she had a complaint. He said to her, "Man is a medicine, and the stomach is a house of disease. Let each man eat of what he is accustomed to eat."

'Ali, may Allah be pleased with him, said that the stomach is a seat of disease, and that not eating is the main remedy, and that habit is second nature. Al-Qadi Abu Ay'ali has related these sayings.

So is it necessary to go without food? – Truly hunger is a cure for excess.

The saying of the Prophet, may Allah bless him and grant him peace, that the stomach is a house of disease, means that one should eat less and ignore the desire for food. However habit is like the nature of man, which is why habit is called second nature. It is indeed a great source of strength for the body, and it is a support in preserving good health. It is because of this that the Prophet, may Allah bless him and grant him peace, said that every man should hold on to his habits.

Abu Nu'aim has related that 'Ayesha said, "Whenever the Prophet, may Allah bless him and grant him peace, took to his tent during the winter, he liked to sleep inside for the first time on a Thursday night – and whenever he came out during the summer, he liked to sleep outside for the first time on a Thursday night."

According to physicians, the temperament of the self should follow the constitution of the body, as has already been stated. When the body is mid-way between being hungry and being full, between being asleep and being awake, and a balance is present, then the self is alert and dynamic and eager for what is good – but when it is weighed down with excesses and extravagances, then the self is distraught. And that is why the Prophet, may Allah bless him and grant him peace, said, "I sleep and I get up. I fast and I break my fast." This is a hadith.

3
Principles of Treatment

Whoever is given the right to practice the treatment of disease must pay attention to age, habit, function and occupation in his treatment. It will not be easy for him to treat a very old man, or a glutton, or a young child, or a person who is very tired, or someone who is in charge of a public bath, or someone whose faculties are weak, or a hypochondriac, or someone whose body is very weak, or a very fat person, or a dark person, or someone with an ulcer, or anyone in very hot or very cold weather, or anyone who is already accustomed to taking medicine – and of these things we have already spoken.

Medicine should not be taken before digestion is complete. Taking a hot bath before taking medicine helps the medicine. Sleeping after taking a weak medicine either stops its action altogether, or makes it even weaker – however after a strong medicine, it makes its action even stronger.

Avoid eating after taking medicine until it has taken effect.

If a man does not like the medicine, then he should chew some tarragon, or vine leaves, or smell some onion, before he takes his medicine – and if he fears that he may vomit, he should stretch his limbs as much as possible, or chew some bitter pomegranates, or rhubarb, or apples. Whoever gets the gripes should drink a little hot water, or walk about a little. And when the medicine has taken effect, then he should make himself vomit by using hot water. After he has vomited, he should take a few fleawort seeds in apple juice. Then after an hour he should have some soup.

No man should take two purges on the same day.

For diseases of the brain, a man should be bled from the cephalic vein; for diseases of the chest, from the basilic vein – and from the median vein for both of them. Bleeding from the salvatella vein is practised on the right side for diseases of the liver, and on the left for diseases of the spleen. The short saphenous vein is used to remedy the pain from sciatica and gout, and the long saphenous vein for producing a free flow during menstruation.

Scarification on the two thighs is almost like blood letting. It increases the menstrual flow. It is performed on the back for ophthalmia, halitosis, and headache.

Enemas are good for colic and stomach ache. The best time to administer them is in the cool of the evening, and in the cool of the morning.

Whenever it is possible to use a gentle remedy, do not use something more powerful instead. Go from the weak to the stronger, if the weak proves to be of no use. Do not content yourself with a single remedy in your treatment, for the constitution of the patient will grow accustomed to it, and so its benefit will diminish.

If you are in doubt about the diagnosis, do not attack the disease with any medicine at all, until the whole matter is clear.

When a dietary regime in itself is sufficient, then do not resort to medicines.

Hippocrates said, "May the physician be given strength from God the Almighty, and obedience towards Him, and good advice, and an understanding of the secrets of disease. Truly he must not administer any fatal drug, nor indicate it, nor point it out. He must not give anything to a woman to cause an abortion. He must keep well away from all pollution and defilement. He must not gaze at women. He must not go in search of excess, idling away his time in pleasure, sleep, eating and drinking, or play – but he must be eager to treat the poor and the people who have nothing. He must be gentle in his speech, kind with his words, and near to God."

This is what Hippocrates said, and he was not one of the believers. I have already said that this Hippocrates was the founder of the Art of Medicine and its leader. He was a Greek physician and their father. He is regarded as having been perfect in the Art of Medicine. It is said that the tomb of Hippocrates is still visited to this day.

Part Two

4

Properties of Foods and Remedies

Simple Remedies

This is how al-Bukhari has divided up the subject in his *Kitab at-Tibb wa'l-Ad'ia*:

Physicians place a medicine in the first degree if it has no obvious effect on the body. If it has some effect, but not a harmful effect, then it is classified as being in the second degree. If it has a harmful effect, but is not fatal, then it is placed in the third degree, but if it goes further than this, then it is placed in the fourth degree and is classified as a poison.

The strength of a remedy is known through experience and by measurement.

The composition of a medicine is either artificial, as in the case of an antidote, or natural, as in the case of milk, which is composed of water, cheese and cream.

If the smell of a remedy is hot, this indicates that it is hot. If there is no smell, then this indicates that it is cold. And in-between is in-between. Furthermore, a sweet-tasting remedy is hot, and similarly a salty-tasting one is hot. A greasy remedy is one that is evenly balanced.

Allah the Almighty says:

And the earth, We have spread it out,
and We have set firm mountains on it,
and We have made every kind of beautiful growth
to grow on it.

(Qur'an: 50.7)

And 'every kind' are full of uses, and the 'beautiful' are beautiful in colour.

A hadith that has been transmitted from al-Hassan through Qatada says that when Sulayman, peace be on him, had finished constructing the Temple, he entered the place of prayer, and suddenly there before him was a bush. When he had finished his prayers, the bush said, "Are you not going to ask me who I am?"

And he replied, "Yes, who are you?" And the bush said, "I am a such-and-such bush, and a remedy for so-and-so, and this and that come from such and so." Then Sulayman ordered that the bush be cut down. And when this had been done, then suddenly another one, similar to it, grew up. And so every day, when he entered the place of prayer, he would meet another of these bushes. In this way he acquired a complete knowledge of all of them, and then wrote his book on Medicine about them, describing the remedies from them.

There is a well-known hadith transmitted from Ibn Abbas that Sulayman, peace be on him, acquired his knowledge of plants as they grew in front of him. He would say to one, "What is your name?" And he would say to another, "What are you for?" And then, depending on their answers, if it was suitable to cultivate the species, cuttings from them would be replanted. And if one contained a remedy, then he would make a record of it. This hadith is taken from Abu Nu'aim.

Alif

Atraj – Lemons

It has been said of the Prophet, may Allah bless him and grant him peace, that he liked to gaze upon a citrus fruit. He said, "The citrus fruit is like a true believer, with a good taste, and a good scent." This is an accepted hadith, taken from al-Bukhari.

The sour citrus is cold and dry. From it is made lemon juice, which is good for hot stomachs. It also strengthens and gladdens the heart, stimulates the appetite, quenches the thirst, satisfies hunger, cures diarrhoea arising from the gall bladder, and expels all bilious diarrhoea and palpitations. It diminishes sorrow and the desolation of the self. It removes ink stains from clothes, and freckles from the face.

The white, pithy matter of the citrus fruit is cold and wet and difficult to digest. It is bad for the stomach, and eating it results in colic.

The seeds, peel, leaves and blossom are hot and dry. The seeds contain the property of an antidote. If two mithqals of them are ground up and put on the sting from a scorpion, this will be beneficial. If a few mithqals are drunk, they will help to counteract all kinds of poisons. The yellow peel is used to make citrus syrup.

This is beneficial in cases of colic, strengthens sexual desires, and stimulates the appetite. It also dissipates wind, although the leaves are stronger and more pleasant for this. The scent of citrus purifies pestilence and foul air.

Masruq said, "I entered the tent of 'Ayesha one day. With her was a man who was completely blind. She was cutting up a citrus for him, and he was eating pieces of it dipped in honey. I said, 'Who is this?' She replied, 'This is the hidden son of my mother who has been given this defect by Allah and His Messenger, may Allah bless him and grant him peace.'"

Athal – Tamarisk

The tamarisk is a large tree. Its leaves resemble those of the other kind of tamarisk and the fig tree. The seeds are like those of the species known as al-'azaba. The properties of the tamarisk resemble the properties of gall-nuts.

It is cold and dry, and in the third degree. It is an astringent for the stomach and a haemostatic.

It has been mentioned by Allah the Almighty:

> ... and in exchange for their two gardens
> We gave them two gardens bearing bitter fruit,
> and tamarisks, and a few lote trees.

(Qur'an: 34.16)

Athmad – Antimony

This is also known as Isfahani collyrium. Its temperament is cold and dry. Antimony strengthens the optic nerve and preserves the health of the eye.

The Prophet, may Allah bless him and grant him peace, said, "The best of all eye-medicines is antimony. It glorifies the sight and makes the eyelashes grow." This hadith has been taken from Abu Daw'ud and at-Tirmidhi. The latter also records another hadith: "The best of your eye-medicines is antimony, which protects the healthy eye, but not the diseased eye."

At-Tirmidhi has related another hadith which says that the Prophet, may Allah bless him and grant him peace, used to have a container in which he kept a collyrium. He used to apply an ointment made from it every night, three times into one eye, and three times into the other. A similar hadith has been transmitted by Anas.

The most pleasing ingredient of the Isfahani collyrium is musk. Abdal-Latif said, "Antimony makes the eyelashes grow, and beautifies the eyes, and makes hearts love them.

Azkhir – Bog-Rush

The bog-rush is hot and dry. It is a mild diuretic and an emmenagogue. It dissolves cold swellings when used as a paste.

The Prophet, may Allah bless him and grant him peace, referred to it.

Aruz – Rice

Rice is the most nourishing of the grain foods after wheat, and excellent in temperament. Some say it is hot and dry, others say cold and dry. It is binding for the bowels, but if cooked with milk is less constipating. If taken with sugar, it will relieve swellings. Rice makes the body fertile and produces more semen. Eating it brings pleasant dreams. Fine rice with the fat of sheep's kidneys is better than a large purge. This is a medical secret.

There is a hadith that says: "The master of your food is meat, and rice comes next."

There is a well-known hadith attributed to 'Ayesha that says: "Rice has healing powers and contains no source of sickness within it."

Arak – Aloes Wood (See also: Sawak and Kabath)

This is the type of aloes wood from which tooth-sticks are made. Abu Hanifa said, "Aloes wood is best for brushing the teeth, for it makes speech more eloquent, frees the tongue, relieves the weakness that comes from disease, stimulates the appetite, and clears the brain. It is better if it is used after being moistened with rosewater.

It has been related that Ibn Abbas said, "Using a tooth-stick has ten benefits: it gives a pleasing perfume to the mouth, it strengthens the gums, it dissolves phlegm, it removes scaling from the teeth, and it prepares the stomach for food. It is in accordance with the shari'ah, and it is pleasing to our Lord. It increases a man's merit, and it gives joy to the angels."

Al-Hadiqa said, "When the Prophet got up in the morning, he used to clean his mouth with a twig of aloes wood." This hadith is taken from al-Bukhari. It is also said that the use of aloes wood increases a man's eloquence. Abu Nu'aim has referred to this.

There are many other well authenticated ahadith on this subject. Some of them associate the Prophet, may Allah bless him and grant him peace, with tooth sticks from the pomegranate or basil. Others associate 'Umar, may Allah be pleased with him, with reed tooth-sticks.

Arnab – Rabbit

The flesh of the rabbit generates spleen. The best meat is from the back and the hind legs. It has been falsely asserted that the female rabbit menstruates, and that the Prophet, may Allah bless him and grant him peace, abandoned eating the flesh of the female rabbit. However, Anas said, "We cooked a rabbit, and Abu Talha sent for the hind legs and took them to the Prophet, may Allah bless him and grant him peace, who received them with thanks."

Asfanakh – Spinach

Spinach is cold and wet and very irritating for the throat and chest, although it acts as a laxative for the bowels.

Astokhodas – Lavender

Lavender is hot and dry. It causes spleen and phlegm to flow and is good for coldness of the brain and its weakness. A syrup is made from it which is useful in hot decoctions.

As – Myrtle

Myrtle is cold and dry, and in the second degree. It puts a stop to diarrhoea. Smelling it soothes a hot headache, as does the powder when used as a paste on ulcers and spots. The paste also strengthens the organs. If one sits in a decoction of it, prolapse of the rectum and uterus is relieved. An ointment of myrtle darkens the hair. The Arabs classify myrtle among the odoriferous herbs.

The Prophet, may Allah bless him and grant him peace, said, "If anyone offers you myrtle as a present, do not refuse it. It is from the Garden." But it should not be used as a tooth stick.

An infusion of myrtle is good for burns. A syrup can also be made from it, but it is no use taking it for a cough, or to stop diarrhoea, unless you also take quince with it. An elixir is made from the seeds of the myrtle.

Ibn Abbas said, "When the Prophet Nuh disembarked from the ark, the first thing that he planted was myrtle." And again, from the same source: "Adam departed from the Garden with three things: myrtle – which is the queen of all the sweet-smelling shrubs in the world, compressed dates – which are queen over all the dates in the world, and a stalk of corn – which is the queen of all the food in the world." This hadith has been related by Abu Nu'aim.

Atriyya – Vermicelli

Vermicelli is hot and very wet. It relieves diarrhoea and sore throats. It takes time to digest, but once digested it provides considerable nourishment.

Aliya – Sheep's Tail

Sheep's tails are hot and wet. They harm the stomach but soothe the nerves.

Anas said, "The Prophet, may Allah bless him and grant him peace, used to prescribe this for sciatica. He used to melt down the tails of four sheep. He would then divide this into three parts, and give one part each day, to be drunk on an empty stomach." This hadith is taken from Ibn Maja.

Anas said, "The Prophet, may Allah bless him and grant him peace, recommended this to more than three hundred people, and they were all cured."

The author of this book says, "This treatment is only right when the pain is due to dryness. In this case, sheep's tails cause relaxation, and the smell causes coction.

The Arabs of the desert improve the quality of their flocks by feeding them on wormwood and artemisia, or on camomile. The first two of these are the most effective in dealing with the pain from sciatica.

Amir Baris – Ambergris

Ambergris is cold and dry. It reduces spleen, relieves thirst, and strengthens the liver. Its juice heightens colour and is used in infusions and pills and in ordinary syrups. A syrup of ambergris is a haemostatic and does not thicken the constitution. This is its special property.

Anisun – Aniseed

Aniseed is hot and dry. It soothes internal pains, dispels wind, increases the flow of menses, milk and semen, and removes all harm from poisons. When used as a collyrium for the eye, it improves the eyesight. This is why snakes go out in search of this plant during the first days of spring and wipe their eyes with it, for during the winter their eyesight grows weak.

Awaz – Goose

The heat of the goose is very great, and it contains some wetness. Its nutritional value lies midway between good and bad.

Ba'

Babunaj – Camomile

Camomile is hot and dry, and in the first degree. It is a mild laxative, a carminative, and an emollient. It dissolves without traction. This is its specific property. When taken orally it increases the urine and the menses. To sit in a decoction of it causes the expulsion of the foetus together with the membranes. It can also be used as a paste, or as a warm enema.

Baqila – Beans

Beans are cold and dry. They produce a lot of wind and are difficult to digest. If a pigeon eats beans, it ceases to lay eggs. If the pubes of a young boy are plastered with mashed beans, the pubic hair will not grow. Beans result in flatulence and cause forgetfulness.

Hippocrates thought that beans were an excellent source of nourishment and good for keeping healthy.

The ill effects of beans can be avoided by eating them with thyme, olive oil and salt.

Badinjan – Aubergines

The black variety generates spleen. A tisane sipped gently is good for piles. It is balanced by having it with meat fried in fat.

The white variety balances all foods.

Burdi – Papyrus

Papyrus is cold. It stops wounds bleeding when there is a strong flow of blood. When used for gargling, it neutralises the smell of garlic and onions. If anyone who has a nose-bleed sniffs up the ashes, the bleeding is stopped.

Ibn Sina said, "It is good for scabs and heals wounds."

Al-Bukhari relates that when the Prophet, may the blessings and peace of Allah be on him and his family, broke a tooth, his daughter Fatima went and found some matting. She set fire to it so that it was reduced to ashes. These she sprinkled on the wounded gum, and the bleeding stopped.

The word 'matting' here means a reed mat, for its ashes, when dry, stop the bleeding.

Al-Bukhari compiled a section in his book specifically on this subject, and called it 'The Healing of Wounds by Using Burned Matting'.

Burquq – Plums

The action of the plum resembles that of the peach (khukh). Please turn to the section on that fruit. (See page 58).

Bun – Coffee Beans

Coffee beans are cold and wet. Coffee is good for dysentery and enteritis. It relieves thirst and softens the constitution. It is said that coffee beans produce wisdom, and should be used with care.

Busur – Unfertilised Female Dates

This type of date is hot and dry. It increases the flow of both spleen and phlegm. It has a cutting action when used in decoctions, enemas and suppositories.

Balah – Fertilised Unripe Dates

These dates are hot, whereas when they are ripe, they are cold. Both tan the stomach.

Ibn Maja said, "Truly the Prophet, may Allah bless him and grant him peace, said, 'Eat fresh and dried dates together, for shaytan has said that Adam, peace be on him, continued to live for as long as he ate fresh dates with dried ones.

According to another hadith, eating dates makes shaytan sad. An-Nasa'i has also related this hadith, but adds that it is not an authentic hadith.

Basal – Onions

The onion is hot and wet. Its virtue is that it remedies changes of water for whoever eats it. It makes food tasty, gives coction to semen, and cuts down phlegm. Sniffing an onion after taking medicine prevents vomiting. Eating meat with onions removes their unpleasant smell.

It has been related from Muawiyya that the Prophet, may Allah bless him and grant him peace, offered food seasoned with onions to some delegates and said, "Eat of this seasoning and say, 'Whoever does not eat of this seasoning, or whatever else diffuses the odour of the earth, will experience harm from its waters and will suffer injury.'"

Onions cause headaches and cloud vision. Too many onions affect the intellect and make a person forgetful. This kind of harm is only caused by raw onions.

The Prophet, may Allah bless him and grant him peace, said, "Whoever eats this vegetable, or whose breath smells of onion or garlic, should not come near us in our mosques, for the angels dislike everything that the sons of men dislike." Al-Bukhari has recorded this hadith. Nevertheless, this prohibition of the Prophet does not make eating onions absolutely forbidden.

Basaq – Saliva

It is said that if someone who is fasting spits on a scorpion, this will kill it.

Batikh – Melon

The green variety is cold and wet, while the yellow tends to be hot. The so-called 'Abdullahi Melon is named after Abu 'Abdullah. The more sweet a melon is, the more hot it is.

When used in an eye lotion, melon makes the eyes shine. It is also a diuretic and is quickly digested. A melon embrocation helps to remove freckles from the face, especially if the embrocation is made from the seeds. It also helps to expel stones from the kidneys and bladder. It also acts as a laxative for any humour that happens to be in the stomach. If tough meat is cooked with the peel of a yellow melon, this makes it tender.

When melon is eaten, it must be fresh, otherwise it may go bad and cause illness. If it is eaten after it has begun to decompose, it must be expelled from the body, because it then takes on bad and poisonous qualities. If a hot sickness results, then the remedy is oxymel; if cold, the remedy is ginger.

The following ahadith about melons have been transmitted:

The Prophet, may Allah bless him and grant him peace, used to eat melon together with fresh dates. He used to say, "One drives out heat, the other, cold." At-Tirmidhi has recorded this hadith.

Abu Daw'ud said, "Among the fruits that the Prophet liked, may Allah bless him and grant him peace, were grapes and melons."

Mashar al-Masghani said, "When my father used to buy melons, he would say, 'Count the ribs on them, my son, for if they come to an odd number, then the melon will be good and ripe, that is, it will be a sweet one.'"

There is also the well-known hadith attributed to Ibn Abbas, that a melon is a food, a drink and a scent. It washes the bladder, cleans the stomach, increases spinal fluid, helps sexual intercourse, clears eyesight, and stops colds. However, the author of this book, is of the opinion that these properties are probably only to be found in the yellow melon.

It is essential that melon is not eaten when you are very hungry.

Butt – Duck

Duck is hotter than chicken.

Baqalat al-Hamqa' – Purslane

This plant is also known as rajlat or farfakh or farfakhin.

Purslane is cold and wet. It helps in dealing with bilious matter, especially when mixed with vinegar, whether it is taken internally or applied externally. It is also good for the teeth. It weakens the sexual appetite, and takes away the desire for food. Whoever spreads purslane on his bed, will never wet his bed, or have nightmares or wet dreams.

It has been related that the Prophet, may Allah bless him and grant him peace, once had an ulcer on his leg. He happened to pass by where some purslane was growing, squeezed some of its juice on his leg, and was cured – whereupon he exclaimed, "Praise be to Allah for you, O purslane, wherever you may be!"

Balut – Acorns

The acorn is cold and dry. It helps stop bed-wetting.

Bandaq – Hazel Nuts

The hazel nut is hot and dry. It slows down the digestion, creates bile, prevents nausea, makes the brain grow, and helps in cases of poisoning.

Banafsaj – Violets

Violets are cold and wet, and in the first degree – although some say that they are hot. Sniffing them, or using them in a paste, relieves sanguineous headaches. Sitting in a decoction of them, or even drinking it, helps with catarrh and relieves internal pains. Violets are used in enemas, infusions, decoctions, pills, suppositories, and pastes.

Boraq – Borax

Borax is hot and dry. It softens the constitution. It is used in several enemas, and in cumin syrup.

Baydha – Eggs

The best of all eggs is a chicken's egg. A soft-boiled egg is better than a hard-boiled egg. In the egg there is perfect balance. An egg that tends to be hard-boiled helps to expel gassy wind. The yoke tends to be hot, the white to be cold.

Rubbing the face with the white of an egg soothes sun-burn, and in a paste it heals burns and prevents scarring. It also relieves eye pains. A soft-boiled egg is good for coughs, roughness in the chest, hoarseness and haemorrhages. It produces plenty of thin chyme. Eggs are a good food – and, finally, they are an aphrodisiac.

It has been related that when someone said to the Prophet, may Allah bless him and grant him peace, "O Messenger of Allah, I complain to Allah the Almighty about my weakness," the Prophet told him to eat eggs. This hadith has been recorded by al-Bayhaqi in his *Sh'ab al-Ayman*.

Ta'

Turab – Dust

Allah the Almighty refers to dust when He says:

**Surely the likeness of Jesus with Allah is
as the likeness of Adam – He created him from dust,
then He said to him: 'Be!' – and he was.**

(Qur'an: 3.59)

The temperament of dust is cold and dry, once its moisture has evaporated.

The Prophet, may Allah bless him and grant him peace, said, "Nothing fills the eye of the sons of Adam except dust," – meaning that man is never satisfied until he is dead.

Tarmus – Lupin

Lupins are hot and dry. When eaten with honey they kill worms, as will a paste made from them when applied to the skin. When powdered they remove scars, and an infusion destroys bed-bugs.

Tabal – Coriander

Tabal contains heat. It is a gentle laxative and is classed among those medicines which are suitable for children.

Turbud – Turpeth

The turpeth is hot and dry. It causes thin phlegm to flow, and also thick if ginger is added. It is used in decoctions, enemas and pills.

Tuffah – Apples

Apples contain wetness which is beneficial. An apple which is sour is more cold than the one which is sweet. Al-Fatahi claims that apples strengthen the heart. Syrup of apples is made from them, which strengthens the faculties and is a good remedy for evil inclinations. Apple jelly is prepared from Nabataean apples. Eating sour apples causes forgetfulness.

Tut – Mulberries

Syrian mulberries are cold and astringent. The effect of eating their core is similar to that of sumach. A jelly can be made from mulberries which alleviates sore throats.

The white mulberry is less nutritious than the red and is bad for the stomach. It should only be eaten before having food, and should be followed by a draught of cold water.

Tamr – Dried Dates

Ali, may Allah be pleased with him, said, "The best dates are the dates called 'al-Burniy'.

Among the hadith concerning dates are the following:

The Prophet, may Allah bless him and grant him peace, said, "The best of all your dates is that of al-Burniy, which drives out disease."

And it has been transmitted by Abu Huraira, "In the sweetness of al-Burniy dates there is no disease.'

Also, the Prophet, may Allah bless him and grant him peace, said, "Your women-folk should eat dates, for whoever makes dates their food will produce children with ease.

As for fresh dates, these were the food of Mary, peace be on her, and if there had been any food that was better, then truly she would have eaten it. Allah the Almighty said:

**And shake the trunk of the palm tree towards you
and fresh ripe dates will drop down on you.**

(Qur'an: 19.25)

The companions used to leave some dates to soak for the Prophet, may Allah bless him and grant him peace, and he would drink the juice the next day – and on the following day he would again ask for it, and drink from it, and then pour away what was left.

Among the ahadith is the saying that eating dates prevents colic.

Ibn Abbas said, "The Prophet, may Allah bless him and grant him peace, used to like the type of date called ''Ajwat,''' and the author of this book says, "Truly the 'Ajwat is an excellent and complete food, and if some butter is added to it then its completeness is perfected – and according to the ahadith the 'Ajwat date is one of the fruits of the Garden."

All of the above ahadith are related by Abu Nu'aim in his *Kitab at-Tibb*.

From Sa'id ibn Abi Waqas comes the well-known hadith, "Whoever has seven 'Ajwat dates for breakfast will not suffer any harm from oppression or sorcery for the whole day." This has been recorded by Al-Bukhari, who considers it to be a sound hadith.

Among the other sound ahadith is this one: "Whoever eats seven dates between dawn and dusk will have no harm come to him between dawn and dusk." The author of this book offers the explanation that by 'dawn' is meant eating the early morning meal each day, and that the 'Ajwat is a type of Madina date which is larger than the al-Sihani date, dark in colour, and planted by the Prophet himself, may Allah bless him and grant him peace. It is clear that it has benefited from the baraka of having been planted by the Prophet. A connection can be seen with the practice of placing two palm branches on the tombs of martyrs and within their graves. Putting these palms there gives them baraka and lessens their pains.

At-Tirmidhi has related a similar hadith. He says that the 'Ajwat is from the Garden, and that there is an antidote against poisons in it. Also 'Ayesha has transmitted this saying of the Prophet, may Allah bless him and grant him peace: "The 'Ajwat date is an excellent remedy." Muslim transmitted this hadith.

It is in accordance with the sunnah for a fasting man to break his fast with dates. The Prophet, may Allah bless him and grant him peace, said, "Whoever can find dates should break his fast with them – and whoever can not find dates should break his fast with water, for truly it is pure." An-Nasa'i transmitted this hadith. The Prophet also said, "As for a house that has no dates, truly those who live in it will go hungry."

Dates are hot and dry. They increase sexual power, especially when combined with pine kernels. However if a person who is suffering from ophthalmia eats them, then he will have headaches and other ill-effects. The Prophet, may Allah bless him and grant him peace, forbade 'Ali, may Allah be pleased with him, to eat dates when he was suffering from ophthalmia, as will be described later, insh'Allah. (See page 128).

The Prophet, may Allah bless him and grant him peace, said that dried dates and dried grapes should not be soaked in water together. He also forbade soaking fresh dates and fresh grapes together.

The ill-effects of dates can be neutralised by eating almonds and poppies.

Tamr Hind – Tamarind

The tamarind is hot and dry, and in the second degree. It provokes a flow of bile, stops vomiting, harms the chest, and is useful in infusions, decoctions, and oxymels. A syrup that takes away thirst is made from them.

Tin – Figs

The best kind of fig is the white fig, when ripe and peeled. Fresh figs are better than dried figs. It contains heat and is very nourishing. It passes swiftly through the intestine. It is the most nourishing of all fruits. It acts as a laxative for the constitution and assuages thirst which is due to phlegm. Figs relieve a chronic cough, act as a diuretic, and clear blockages. Eating figs on an empty stomach is very efficacious in opening up the alimentary tract, especially when eaten with almonds and walnuts.

Abu'd-Darda said, quoting the Prophet, may Allah bless him and grant him peace, "If you are going to say that any fruit has come from the Garden, then truly you should mention the fig, for it is indeed the fruit of the Garden." It has no stone. So eat of it, for it cures piles and helps gout.

Some physicians have said that eating figs for a long time is bad for the body.

And the wild fig is bad for the stomach and a very poor food.

Tha'

Thum – Garlic

Garlic is hot and dry, and in the third degree. It makes wind disappear. A paste made from it blisters the skin. Eating garlic is beneficial after a change in drinking water. It also precipitates menstruation and helps to expel the afterbirth – but it causes headaches and harms the eyesight.

It has been related that the Prophet, may Allah bless him and grant him peace, said, "O 'Ali, eat garlic – and were it not for my being visited by the angel of Allah (Jibril), I would eat it myself." And 'Ali, may Allah be pleased with him, said, "The Prophet, may Allah bless him and grant him peace, advised against eating garlic except when cooked."

Garlic is very good for cold temperaments, for those who are phlegmatic, and for those who have palsy, but it dries up semen. It makes wind disappear, relieves pains caused by the cold, and acts like an antidote for bites. A paste made from it is very good for treating animal bites and scorpion stings. It is also used to remove leeches from the throat, as well as having many other uses.

Anas has transmitted the hadith, "Whoever eats of this vegetable should not enter our mosques." This hadith has also been transmitted by al-Bukhari.

Rue neutralises the smell of garlic.

Thalaj – Snow or Ice

Snow is bad for both the stomach and the liver, especially for those who are weak. Eating snow makes a person thirsty because it absorbs heat.

Jim

Jabn – Cheese

Fresh cheese is cold and wet, while dried cheese is hot and dry. It is moderately good for you. Fresh cheese is a very fattening food, while salty cheese makes you loose weight, although it increases the sexual urge.

It has been related by Umm Salama, "I once offered the Prophet, may Allah bless him and grant him peace, some toasted cheese and he ate it. Then he went out to do the prayer without doing wudu." At-Tirmidhi has transmitted this hadith in his *Ash-Shama'il*. The same hadith is also recorded by al-Muqira.

Toasted cheese is good for ulcers of the bowel and alleviates diarrhoea.

Jarjir – Cress

Physicians call this plant Baqala 'Ayasana. It is hot and wet. It stimulates desire for sexual intercourse.

It has been related that the Prophet, may Allah bless him and grant him peace, said, "Cress is a herb from Ethiopia, and I have seen it growing in the fire of Jahannam."

Jarad – Locust

Locusts are hot and dry, and a very poor food. Most of them cause wasting away.

Ibn Abi Aufi said, "We went on seven raids with the Prophet, may Allah bless him and grant him peace, when we ate locusts on the way. This hadith has been transmitted by al-Bukhari and Muslim.

'Umar, may Allah be pleased with him, said, "The Prophet, may Allah bless him and grant him peace, once expressed a desire for a toasted locust."

The wives of the Prophet, may the blessings and peace of Allah be on him and his family and companions, used to give locusts to one another as presents.

Jazr – Carrots

Carrots are wet and hot. They arouse desire for sexual intercourse and produce a good supply of semen. They also precipitate menstruation and urination.

Jummar – Core of the Date Palm

The core of the date palm is white, cold and wet. It is good for diarrhoea and takes time to be digested.

According to Ibn 'Umar the core of a date palm was once given to the Prophet, may Allah bless him and grant him peace, and he said, "Of all the trees, there is one tree that is blessed with baraka just as the true believers are blessed." By this he meant the palm tree. This hadith comes from al-Bukhari and Muslim.

Juz – Walnut

The walnut is hot and dry. It causes headaches. It is difficult to digest and is bad for the stomach. Fresh walnuts are better than dried ones. A mixture of walnuts and honey is good for sore throats.

Ibn Sina said, "Eating figs, walnuts and rue is a remedy for all poisons and their like."

Dioscorides said, "Take walnuts both before and after eating poison."

It has been related that al-Mahdi said, "I entered the house of al-Mansur, and saw him eating cheese and walnuts, so I said to him, 'What is this?' and he said, 'My father told me about someone who once saw the Prophet, may Allah bless him and grant him peace, eating cheese and walnuts, and so he asked him about it, and the Prophet replied, "Cheese is a disease and walnuts are a medicine. If you combine the two, then you have a remedy."'" This hadith is recorded in *Al-Wasila*.

Ha'

Habbah – Seeds

Habbat'l-Sauda – Coriander Seeds

Al-Bukhari says that coriander seeds are hot and dry, and in the third degree. Abu Huraira has transmitted a well-known hadith, "Coriander seeds are for you, because they are a cure for all diseases except cancer – and that is a fatal disease." This hadith is also recorded by al-Bukhari and Muslim.

What the Arabs call 'habbat'l-sauda', the Persians call 'shuniz'. According to a hadith which comes from al-Hassan, this word means 'mustard'. However al-Harawi says that the word means 'fruit of the terebinth tree' and nothing else. Abdal-Latif says that the word means 'black cumin', which is also known as Indian cumin, and that the uses of cumin are many, and that therefore it is universally accepted as a panacea. 'Universally' should mean 'everywhere', but here the word means 'for most diseases' – and even then this statement is an exaggeration. Allah the Almighty says:

> ... and she has been given everything ...

> (Qur'an: 27.23)

In saying this He may have been referring to medicine, but this is in the knowledge of Allah and in the knowledge of the Prophet, may Allah bless him and grant him peace, alone. Allah has withheld this knowledge from us, but the Prophet has made us aware of its existence.

Another similar example is this: The Prophet, may Allah bless him and grant him peace, has told us that whoever has seven 'Ajwat dates for breakfast will not suffer from any harm or sorcery on that day. Here is another example: The Prophet, may Allah bless him and grant him peace, has told us that one wing of a fly carries a disease, and the other its cure. And there are many other similar examples. These revelations are from among the miracles of the Prophet, may Allah bless him and grant him peace.

Coriander seeds are useful in counteracting all diseases that are cold and wet. They are also used in treating hot diseases when combined with other remedies, in order to accelerate their penetration. An example of a similar course of action is when physicians combine saffron with camphor in a pill.

Coriander seeds remove wind, leucoderma patches, and recurring phlegmy fever. They clear blockages, dissolve wind, dry up soggy stomachs, and never fail to increase the flow of urine, menses and milk. If they are ground up with vinegar, made into a paste, and rubbed on the abdomen, they kill intestinal worms. Thus they are also known as 'worm-seed'. They also cure colds. If they are boiled in fat, they are good for treating baldness, warts and delusions. An ointment made of coriander seeds stimulates the growth of the beard and stops hair turning grey.

A draught of one mithqal is good for treating shortness of breath and tarantula bites, and if it is ground up and taken dry every day, then it is good in cases of dog bite and helps to prevent death. The smoke from burning the seeds drives away flying insects. When eaten with bread, the seeds remove wind and relieve headaches. A paste made from them is good for palsies, facial paralysis, all types of hemicrania, apoplexy, stupor, amnesia, vertigo and giddiness.

Thus the uses of coriander are many. Whoever desires to know them all must research the lengthy works of physicians – for they have all been described by them so that they will not be forgotten. I have only given a summary here. And if the physicians are aware of all the uses of this plant, then you can be quite sure that the Prophet knew them too, he being the first and last of all teachers, may the blessings and peace of Allah be on him and his family and companions – and may we be protected on the Day of Judgement, the day which is constantly remembered by those who remember, and whose remembrance is forgotten by those who forget.

Habb al-Sanubar – Pine Kernels

Pine kernels are hot and dry. They increase semen. They are made, with pomegranate, into a bitter-sweet antidote, and are included in philosopher's syrup.

Habb ar-Rashad (also called Hurf) – Cress Seeds

Cress seeds are hot and dry. They are a remedy for tenesmus when it is caused by the cold. They also activate semen. The smoke from burning them drives away insects and dissolves wind and colic. Their effect is similar to that of mustard seeds.

It has been related that the Prophet, may Allah bless him and grant him peace, said, "What are the two basic cures? They are aloes wood and mustard seeds."

Abu 'Ubayda said, "'Hurf' means 'unripe grapes'." These are cold and dry. They destroy bile. An infusion made from them stops diarrhoea and vomiting, and stimulates sexual desire. An infusion made with unripe grapes and mint is used to remove nausea.

Harir – Silk

Silk is hot and dry. The best silk is raw silk. It is classified as a stimulant. Wearing silk stops lice spreading – although Ibn Sina says the opposite.

Al-Bukhari and Muslim have transmitted the hadith that the Prophet, may Allah bless him and grant him peace, allowed Ibn 'Auf and Zubair to wear silk because of their itchiness. When they complained about lice while they were on a raid, he permitted them to wear silk shirts – which is very strengthening for the heart, although it is haram for men.

Thus there is proof in the hadith that it is halal to treat oneself with what is normally haram, and so to be cured in accordance with the law of healing, for this is permitted in the case of treating the itch. Thus it is permitted in this situation, even though Malik normally forbade it.

From Abu Musa comes the well-known hadith that Allah has made it halal for women to wear gold and silk, but He has made it haram for their men-folk. This is a sound hadith.

Abu'd-Darda has transmitted another well-known hadith that Allah has created both disease and cure, and that He has made a remedy for every disease – and this is the remedy that people should use, and they should not be treated by haram means. So use medicine, but not haram medicine. Abu Daw'ud has also related this hadith.

The saying of the Prophet, may Allah bless him and grant him peace, "Use medicine," is an order. Even the mildest form of order is a command. Whatever is prohibited implies that it is haram. If anyone were to say that the Prophet's order in this case makes wearing silk halal, then we would reply, "This is certainly the case, since it has been preceded by a prohibition." A similar example is when Allah says:

... and when you have left the Haram, then you may hunt ...

(Qur'an: 5.2)

And also, He says:

O you who believe, when the call for prayer is heard
for the day of the jumu'a,
then hasten to the remembrance of Allah
and leave your trading.
That is better for you, if you only knew.

And when the prayer is over,
then go out into the land
and seek Allah's bounty,
and remember Allah much
so that you will be successful.

(Qur'an: 62.9-10)

Truly the Prophet, may Allah bless him and grant him peace, used to treat himself with medicine. According to one well-known hadith, Abu Huraira has related, "Whoever treats himself with halal medicines will be cured, and as for whoever treats himself with haram medicines, Allah will not cure him."

Another hadith relates that the Prophet, may Allah bless him and grant him peace, was asked about wine, as to whether it could be used as a medicine, and he replied, "Wine is not a medicine." This hadith has been transmitted by Abu Daw'ud and at-Tirmidhi.

It has been related by Abu Huraira that the Prophet, may Allah bless him and grant him peace, forbade using anything that is detested as a remedy. Al-Waki' says that by this he meant the use of incantations. However al-Bayhaqi has recorded the hadith that Ibn al-'Arabi said that the word 'detested' in the Arabic language means anything that is hateful: thus as far as speech is concerned, it means 'abuse'; as far as the deen is concerned, it means 'heresy'; as far as food is concerned, it means 'haram'; and as far as drink is concerned, it means 'harmful'.

'Uthman ibn Abdar-Rahman says that a physician once talked of using a frog in his treatment. The Prophet, may Allah bless him and grant him peace, rebuked him and forbade him from killing it. This hadith has been transmitted by Abu Daw'ud and an-Nasa'i.

It has been related by Tariq ibn Suwayd, "I told the Prophet, may Allah bless him and grant him peace, that we grew grapes and pressed out the juice and drank it (after it had fermented), and he said, 'Do not do this.' Then I went back to him and said, 'I cure the sick with it,' and he replied, 'Truly that is not healing – it is creating illness.'" This hadith has been transmitted by Muslim, Abu Daw'ud and at-Tirmidhi, and it is an accurate and reliable hadith.

Al-Khattabi said, "It is described as a disease, because drinking (fermented) grape juice involves wrong action."

Indeed it is quite true that there is no benefit to be gained from drinking wine. When the asker asked about it, he already knew that it involved wrong action, but he was enquiring about any beneficial properties that it might nevertheless still have – but the Prophet, may Allah bless him and grant him peace, rejected this and denied any such possibility. And Allah knows everything.

It does appear that wine is a remedy for some diseases, but the Prophet, may Allah bless him and grant him peace, viewed it from beyond the limits of this world, and within the limits of the next world – and considered it not in terms of what is natural, but in terms of what is halal.

Someone else has pointed out that Allah in His Glory deprived wine of all benefits when He made it haram. And Allah knows everything.

Please note that the word 'khamr' and 'khamrah' (meaning 'wine' – and by analogy anything that is alcoholic or intoxicating) appears in both the masculine and the feminine form, as does the word 'tamr' and 'tamrah' (meaning 'date').

Finally, wearing silk is also useful for treating melancholia.

Hilba – Fenugreek

Fenugreek is hot and dry. If a decoction of it is drunk, it precipitates menstruation. It is also useful in cases of colic, and is sometimes used in sour enemas and cleansing decoctions.

It has been related that the Prophet, may Allah bless him and grant him peace, once said, "If my community had only known what there is in fenugreek, they would have bought it and paid its weight in gold. The author of *Al-Wasila* has transmitted this hadith.

Fenugreek strengthens the heart. Among its special properties is that it ameliorates the stink of excrement and smelly sweat and urine.

Halwa – Sweets

Sweets made from sugar are hot and wet. They ease sore throats and are good for coughs. It is good to eat them.

Sweets made from honey are incomparable. They are best suited for the phlegmatic. 'Ayesha, may Allah be pleased with her, said, "The Prophet, may Allah bless him and grant him peace, loved sweets and honey." Al-Bukhari has recorded this hadith.

A sweet made from dates and butter (known as 'khabis') is very good for those who suffer from spleen, from phthisis, and from hectic fever.

Hammas – Chick-peas

The chick-pea is hot and wet. The effect of the dark pea is stronger than that of the red, and the effect of the red is stronger than that of the pale.

The chick-pea produces wind. It also stimulates sexual desires and increases semen and milk. It beautifies the complexion and does to the body what leavening does to dough.

Some physicians have said, "There are three things that are needed for fruitful sexual intercourse. All of them are present in the chick-pea."

Hamam – Dove

The wild dove is less wet than the tame dove, and a young dove is more wet than an old one. Eating the flesh of doves increases sexual energy. Eating dove's flesh cooked with sour grapes, or eating the flesh of the fine-eyed dove, heals cases of paraesthesia – that is, where legs and arms have gone to sleep – and cases of flaccidity and tremors.

According to Hussayn, it is said, "Do not go looking for their nests at night, for truly at night they are secure.

Himar al-Wahash – Wild Ass

The wild ass is hot and dry. It generates thick blood. Its fat is good for back and kidney pains, and for chills.

They say that Qatada was renowned for his hunting them. Al-Bukhari also confirms this.

Handhal – Colocynth

The colocynth is hot and dry, and in the third degree. One should avoid the pips and only use the pith mashed with pistachio nut kernels. A single colocynth on a bush is a deadly poison.

Colocynth produces an extreme flow of phlegm.

The Prophet, may Allah bless him and grant him peace, said, "The colocynth resembles the hypocrite. It has no scent and tastes bitter."

Hintat – Wheat

Wheat is hot and half way between wet and dry. Eating raw wheat results in intestinal worms and wind.

Flour should be eaten the same day that it is ground, and after having been kneaded.

Hinna – Henna

Henna is cold and dry, although some say that it contains heat. It is used for treating mouth ulcers, stomatitis and hot swellings. Decoctions of henna are good for burns. When used as a dye it reddens the hair and beautifies it. It is also useful in treating infections of the nails. If someone who catches small-pox stains his body with henna at the onset of the disease, then the pox will not come near his two eyes.

It has been related that Umm Salama said, "The Prophet, may Allah bless him and grant him peace, never suffered from a wound or a thorn without putting henna on it." At-Tirmidhi and al-Bayhaqi have transmitted this hadith. In the *History* of al-Bukhari, it is written that a man once complained to the Prophet of a pain in his head. All that he said in reply was, "Then have a hot bath." And to the one who complained to him of a pain in his legs, all that he said was, "Dye them with henna." Abu Daw'ud transmitted this hadith, and also records the hadith that he said, "There is no plant dearer to Allah than henna."

It has been related by Abu Huraira that the Prophet, may Allah bless him and grant him peace, said, "The Jews and the Christians do not dye themselves with henna, so act differently to them." Abu Huraira and Abu Daw'ud transmitted this hadith.

Ahmad ibn Hanbal said, "I can not love any man who fails to dye his grey hair in order not to resemble the People of the Book." For the Prophet, may Allah bless him and grant him peace, once said, "They did not dye their hair and so truly they resembled the People of the Book." This is what has been transmitted by at-Tirmidhi, and indeed it is a good and sound hadith.

Ahmad said, "Dye your hair with henna. It is preferable that you do it – even if it is only once rather than not at all – so that you do not come to resemble the Jews." And Abu Dharr said that the Prophet, may Allah bless him and grant him peace, once remarked, "The best thing with which to conceal your grey hair is henna or indigo."

Abu Rafi' once said, "I was with the Prophet once, may Allah bless him and grant him peace, when he stroked his beard with his hand and said, "To you belongs the prince of dyes, which benefits the eyesight and increases sexual energy." It has been reported by Anas, "They dyed themselves with henna, and so truly they became younger, more fertile, and more potent." Abu Nu'aim has also recorded these two statements.

Al-Muwaffaq Abdal-Latif said, "The colour of henna is the colour of fire, and it is loved because it arouses the faculty of love. Its scent is a perfume."

Our forefathers did indeed usually dye themselves with henna – for example, Muhammad ibn Hanifa and Ibn Sirin used to wash with it; Abu Bakr used to dye himself with it; and 'Umar and Abu 'Ubayda used to bath in it. Indeed 'Umar dyed his beard yellow with it. Also, he said that he saw the Prophet with a beard dyed yellow, may the blessings and peace of Allah be on him and them.

In al-Bukhari there is the saying of Umm Salama, "I took a hair of the Prophet, may Allah bless him and grant him peace, out to them, and clearly it had been dyed with indigo and henna." Anas said, "I saw the hair of the Prophet, may Allah bless him and grant him peace, and it had been dyed." And there is the other hadith of Umm Salama, "Truly the Prophet, may Allah bless him and grant him peace, never suffered from a cut or a thorn in his skin without putting henna on it."

Indeed the cure for cuts is whatever dries out their moisture and whatever stimulates the faculty of causing tissue growth – and this is exactly what henna does, for it dries out the excess moisture which otherwise prevents fresh tissue growth in cuts. And as for thorns, henna has the capacity to counteract the flaccidity of an organ and so assist in the expulsion of a thorn.

If henna blossom is placed in woollen clothing, then this perfumes it and stops it from being eaten by moths. Some experienced people say that if henna leaves are soaked in water and squeezed out, and if that water is then taken daily for twenty days – 40 drachms of liquid with 10 drachms of sugar – then it assists in the treatment of leprosy in its early stages. If, after eating lamb's meat along with this, the patient is not cured, then there is no cure left for him.

Kha'

Khubbaza – Mallow

Mallow is cold and wet. It relaxes the constitution and the throat and helps whoever has a cough. Its seeds are used in emollient enemas and such like. A decoction used as a douche is good for an itchy anus.

Khubz – Bread

Allah the Almighty says:

> ... Now send one of you with this money of yours to the city,
> and let him see what food is purest
> and bring you some of it to eat
> – and let him behave with courtesy ...

(Qur'an: 18.19)

Physicians have said that the best bread is bread baked in a circular brick oven – well-baked and using fine flour. The temperament of such bread is hot and rather dry. It should not be eaten until it has cooled down, for truly its heat makes you thirsty. The best time to eat it is on the same day that it was kneaded – and when it is stale or pasty, it makes the constitution constipated.

The next best bread is that which is cooked in an upright oven. Any other kind of bread is no good.

The less bran there is in bread, the more slowly it is digested, but the more nourishing it is. Soft bread is more nutritious and easier to digest. Bread crumbs produce wind and are slow to be digested. Bread which is like cake produces thick humours. Bread made with milk creates blockages but is very nourishing; it passes down through the intestine slowly. Barley bread is cooling and causes wind. Bread made from chick-peas is slow to digest and needs a lot of salt.

'Ayesha is credited with transmitting the well-known hadith that has been attributed to the Prophet, may Allah bless him and grant him peace, "Honour bread, for Allah has made the earth and the sky its servants."

Khukh – Peaches

The peach is cold and wet. It relaxes the stomach and eases the bowel. It is better to eat it before a meal rather than after a meal. A syrup which is good for bilious fevers, and relaxes the system, and quenches thirst, is made from it. It is used in laxative infusions and decoctions.

Kharnub – Carob

Carob is cold and astringent, good for the intestine, but bad for the stomach. Its juice tends to be hot and is agreeable to the bowel.

According to tradition, the staff of Sulayman, peace be on him, was made from the carob tree.

Khardal – Mustard

Mustard is hot and dry, and in the fourth degree. It reduces phlegm. Too much mustard causes blindness. One of its properties is that it clears blockages in the brain.

Khass – Lettuce

Lettuce is cold and wet. It has more nourishment in it than all the other vegetables. Eating it increases the softness of the constitution and helps those who suffer from delirium. However it dries up semen and diminishes desire for sexual intercourse. Constantly eating lettuce weakens the eyesight.

Khashkhash – Poppies

Poppies are cold and dry, and in the second degree. They cause intoxication and sleep.

Khatmi – Marsh Mallow

The marsh mallow is moderately hot. A decoction made from the roots helps in cases of tenesmus and looseness of the bowel. The seeds are used in softening enemas.

Khall – Vinegar

Vinegar has both hot and cold elements, but the cold predominates. It is good for inflammation of the stomach. It has an adverse effect on the splenic humour, but counteracts phlegm. It is good for erysipelas, herpes, scabies and burns. When mixed with rose ointment in an infusion, it is good for hot headaches. Gargling with vinegar alleviates toothache and relieves pain, whether hot or cold. It can produce burning in the anus, but helps the digestion.

The Prophet, may Allah bless him and grant him peace, said, "Vinegar is a comfort for man." Muslim has transmitted this hadith. Another well-known hadith has also been transmitted: "Allah has put blessing in vinegar, for truly it was the seasoning used by the prophets before me." And al-Bayhaqi has transmitted this hadith: "A household which has vinegar will never suffer from poverty."

A syrup called oxymel is made with vinegar, and there is a conserve of roses which in Iraq is called 'syrup of vinegar'. It safeguards the health of those who have hot constitutions and alleviates infected fevers. It diminishes the semen, and if taken at breakfast, it reduces sexual potency.

Khamr – Wine

Wine is prepared from particular kinds of grapes. The author of this book would like to point out that this is the opinion of the Hanafi madhdhab. However the view of the majority of the 'ulama' is that anything that intoxicates comes within the definition of 'wine', as has already been demonstrated and discussed in the section dealing with drinking wine. (See pages 53 – 54).

Khamat

Abu 'Ubayda says that the word 'khamat' can be applied to any tree with thorns, but others say that the word only applies to aloes wood. I have already described the properties of aloes wood, (see page 36), and these also sufficiently describe khamat.

Khilal – Tooth-stick

There is no need to describe this further, as it has already been dealt with in describing aloes wood. (See page 36).

Khiyar – Cucumber

The type of cucumber called khiyar is colder and more substantial than the type called qitha. (See page 85). The best kind has small seeds. It should be eaten with honey. The best part is the pith.

Khiyar Shanbar – Cassia

Cassia contains heat. It precipitates a flow of spleen and bile. Gargling with cassia and milk is good for inflamed throats. Cassia relieves a full stomach. Cassia is balanced by almond ointment. It is also an ingredient in various decoctions, enemas and linctuses.

Dal

Darsini – Cinnamon

Cinnamon is hot and dry, and in the third degree. It contains a fragrance which fortifies the stomach. A mouthwash with cinnamon in it, taken on an empty stomach, is good for bad eyesight. Cinnamon also strengthens ointments.

Darunaj – Leopard's Bane

Leopard's Bane is dry, and in the second degree. It improves the eyesight, increases the flow in menstruation and urination, and eating it helps to relax the constitution. It is used, when decocted, in lotions and infusions, as well as in powders.

Dabas – Syrup of Grapes

Syrup of grapes is hot and wet. It generates turbid blood, but this can be remedied by using almonds, poppies and sesame oil.

When 'Umar, may Allah be pleased with him, went to Syria, he found people preparing syrup of grapes. He asked about it, and was told that it was made from grape juice which was boiled until one third of it had evaporated. So then he said, "Truly what was haram in it has disappeared, and what is left is halal – what was harmful in it has indeed gone, and its pleasant aroma remains. So tell the Muslim army to drink it and increase their strength!"

Ibn Khalil relates this anecdote in his brief *History of the Conquest of Syria*.

Dajaj – Chicken

Chicken is the best of bird meats. It is hot and wet, and in the first degree. It is light on the stomach, easy to digest, and good for the humours. It fortifies the brain and semen and makes the complexion more beautiful. It sharpens the intellect of anyone who eats it regularly, but it causes gout. The best chicken is a hen that has never laid an egg.

A cock is more hot and less wet. The meat of an old bird is a remedy for colic and impotency. It is easily digested and full of nourishment.

The Prophet, may Allah bless him and grant him peace, said, "Whenever you hear a cock crowing, then praise Allah for its excellence, for truly it has just seen an angel."

Among the sound hadith is one that says that the Prophet, may Allah bless him and grant him peace, ate chicken meat and chicken soup.

Ibn al-Baytar says that eating chicken meat soothes heart-burn. It is swiftly digested, relaxes the constitution, and increases the blood supply.

Dhal

Dhabab – Flies

Physicians have said very little about flies, other than that they are very useful when rubbed on wasp and scorpion stings, and that swollen eyelids can be cured if rubbed with them.

The Prophet, may Allah bless him and grant him peace, said, "If a fly falls into the drink of any one of you, then first push it right in and then remove it, for truly one of its wings carries a disease – and the other its cure. This hadith has been transmitted by Muslim. Al-Bukhari said, "If a fly falls into anyone's cup, then he should put a lid over it.

According to the hadith transmitted by Ibn Maja and Abu Daw'ud, the poison is in the front wings, and the remedy is in the back wings. Al-Khattabi has related that some people who were ill-disposed towards him commented on this hadith and said, "How can it be that both illness and healing are present in the wings of a fly? And how do you know that the disease is in the front wings, and the cure in the back wings?" And he replied, "These are questions that a fool asks, or someone who is nearly a fool – for truly He who renews the soul, that is the soul which all creatures have in common, has given it the quality of being mid-way between hot and cold, and wet and dry. Now these temperaments are opposites of each other, and if Allah has been able to create thousands of combinations of them, then surely it can not be denied that He has placed both a poison and its cure in different creatures. Take the bee, for example. He has inspired it to build its home from wax, and to make honey there. Similarly, He has inspired the snipe to conserve its energy until it is needed. It is He who has created the fly, and given it the gift of both back and front wings – and in everything, I maintain, there is evidence of the Tawhid of Allah."

Some physicians have written that the fly which is known as 'Spanish fly' has a poison in one wing and its remedy in the other.

Dhahab – Gold

Gold is evenly balanced. It contains a subtle heat. It is used in carminatives, and fortifies the heart. It is good for the mouth, and sucking it relieves a sore throat. When it is used in cautery, it does not cause blistering and healing is swift.

The Prophet, may Allah bless him and grant him peace, forbade the use of gold and silver containers, but their use as medicines is permitted.

Ra'

Rawand – Rhubarb

Rhubarb is hot and dry, although some say it is cold. The best is fresh and without the roots. It helps to dissolve blockages in the liver, and it relieves chronic fevers and those who are afflicted with dropsy.

Ratb – Fresh Dates

These have already been described under the heading of dried dates, under the letter 'Ta". (See page 45).

Fresh dates are hot and moist. They cause wind. When taken with an oxymel, or with bitter pomegranates, they balance a hot constitution.

It has been forbidden by the Prophet, may Allah bless him and grant him peace, to add fresh dates to any infusion.

Rumman – Pomegranates

Allah the Almighty says:

In which there is fruit, and date palms, and pomegranates ...

(Qur'an: 55.68)

The sweet pomegranate is hot and wet. Drinking it stops coughs. Eating it after a meal prevents an upset stomach. The best type of pomegranate is the 'Imlisi'.

The bitter pomegranate is cold and dry. It is good for bile. Syrup of pomegranates, seasoned with mint, is made from it. This stops vomiting and fortifies the stomach.

The bitter-sweet pomegranate is in between these two.

All these types of pomegranates reduce palpitations.

Abu Nu'aim has transmitted the hadith, which he heard from Anas, that the Prophet, may Allah bless him and grant him peace, was asked about pomegranates and that he replied, "There is not a pomegranate which does not have a pip from one of the pomegranates of the Garden in it." And another hadith states, "No pomegranate grows ripe without being watered by a drop of the water of the Garden." And yet another hadith goes, "No one eats pomegranates without his heart being moved and shaytan fleeing from him." And here is a hadith from 'Ali, may Allah be pleased with him: He said, "Whoever eats pomegranates has the light of Allah in his heart!"

Whenever Ibn 'Abbas spotted a pomegranate pip, he would pick it up and eat it. People asked him why he did this, and he replied, "I truly believe that there is not a single pomegranate on earth which does not contain one pip from the pips of the Garden – and perhaps this pip is the one!"

Eating pomegranates has various effects on a man: Eating the pith dyes the stomach green. Likewise, al-Amadi said that he heard Ibn Butlan say, "If anyone eats pomegranate stalks for three days, he will be free from ophthalmia for a year."

Ramal – Sand

The Prophet, may Allah bless him and grant him peace, said, "If you bury anyone suffering from dropsy in sand, his disease will diminish and not return."

Rihan – Sweet Basil

Basil is hot. Its aroma strengthens the heart. A sprinkling of basil in water induces sleep.

Al-Bukhari has reported the hadith of the Prophet, may Allah bless him and grant him peace, "Whoever is offered sweet basil should not refuse it, for it is easy to take and has a pleasing scent."

Zay

Zubd – Butter

Butter is hot and wet, and in the first degree. It is a decoctant and a solvent. The best butter is fresh butter. It is good for constipation and dry coughs, but it weakens the desire for food. When 'dried out' by being mixed with honey and dates, it helps to expel the odd appetites that women may have when pregnant.

It has been related by Abu Daw'ud that 'Ali, may Allah be pleased with him, used to enjoy butter and dates. And Abu Nu'aim has related that the Prophet, may Allah bless him and grant him peace, once said to 'Ayesha, "I love you more than I do butter and honey."

Zabib – Dried Grapes

The best dried grapes or currants are the large ones, with a lot of flesh and small pips.

Currants are hot and wet. They are warming, thirst-making, and fatten cold bodies. When combined with oxymel they balance hot constitutions. The seeds irritate the stomach, but are beneficial when ground up and added to powders made from the seeds of the bitter pomegranate.

It has been related that Tamim ad-Dari once gave some currants to the Prophet, may Allah bless him and grant him peace, who, once they had been placed in his hands, said to his companions, may Allah be pleased with them, "Eat!", and so they enjoyed their meal of currants.

Currants drive away fatigue, calm down anger, sharpen the nerves, help to make intercourse pleasant, expel phlegm, and clear up the complexion. 'Ali, may Allah be pleased with him, said, "Whoever eats twenty-one red currants every day, will never find anything upsetting in his body."

Both of the above hadith have been transmitted by Abu Nu'aim.

It has been related that Ibn Abbas once said, "Eat currants, but spit out the stones – for in the stones there is illness, but in the flesh there is healing." And from the same source we have learned that the Prophet, may Allah bless him and grant him peace, used to have currants soaked in water for him, and that he used to drink it either on that day, or the next. Then he would have whatever was left either drunk or else thrown away.

It has been related in a hadith that a servant was once thirsty, but the Prophet, may Allah bless him and grant him peace, forbade him from putting a mixture of dates and currants into the same water to soak. This is a hadith from al-Bukhari.

Az-Zuhri said, "I love to retain ahadith, and so I eat currants." And az-Zuhri indeed used to eat currants and refuse to eat sour apples.

Truly eating currants puts more things right than eating dates. And whoever eats currants, pistachio nuts and gum drops every day on an empty stomach will indeed have a powerful brain.

Zaqqum

This is the name of a gum tree in the Hijaz. Allah the Almighty says that the tree of Zaqqum is the food of the wrong-doers in the akhira:

> Surely We have made it a torment for wrong-doers:
> surely it is a tree that grows in the heart of Hell,
> with its fruits like the heads of shayatin,
> and surely they have to eat from it
> and fill their bellies with it
> and then drink boiling water after that.

(Qur'an: 37.63-67)

Z'afran – Saffron

Saffron is hot and dry. It expels wind and fortifies the soul. Ibn 'Umar has transmitted the hadith that the Prophet, may Allah bless him and grant him peace, forbade the wearing of garments dyed with saffron and such like during the month of Muharram. This hadith has been related by al-Bukhari. And the reason for this is because saffron fortifies the essence of the soul and stimulates sexual intercourse – and sexual intercourse is forbidden during Muharram.

Zanjabil – Ginger

Ginger is mentioned in the Qur'an:

> And there they are given a drink from a cup
> in which there is a mixture of zanjabil.
>
> **(Qur'an: 76.17)**

Ginger is hot and dry in the third degree, and dry in the second. It contains an excess of wetness. It helps the digestion, stimulates sexual intercourse, and dissolves wind. If turpeth is too weak when used as a purge, or if there is oedema, then its strength is increased by adding ginger to it. It also makes thick phlegm more fluid. Confections made with ginger soothe the stomach. It helps in old age.

It has been reported by Abu Sa'id that a Byzantine emperor once gave a jar of ginger to the Prophet, may Allah bless him and grant him peace, who made all of his companions eat a piece of it, may Allah be pleased with them.

Zayt wa Zaytun – Olive Oil and Olives

These are wet for the bowels. If the oil is squeezed from fresh olives, it is cold and dry. The oil which comes from fully matured olives is hot and moderately wet. The older it is, the hotter it is.

When olive oil is used as a balm, it fortifies the hair and the limbs and delays old age. Drinking the oil is beneficial in cases of poisoning. It keeps the bowels on the move, soothes pains, expels worms, as well as having many other uses. All balms weaken the stomach – except olive oil. The best kind of olive oil is known as 'Infaq'.

From Ibn 'Umar comes the well-known hadith, "Use olive oil and anoint yourself with it, because it is **'from a blessed tree'** (Qur'an: 24.35)." Al-Bayhaqi has also transmitted this hadith.

As regards the olive tree, Allah says:

And a tree that grows on mount Sinai
which provides oil – and enjoyment for those who eat it.

(Qur'an: 23.20)

For olive oil is the best of seasonings.

And again, at-Tirmidhi says, "Eat olive oil and anoint yourself with it."

And from 'Alqama ibn 'Amar comes the hadith: "Every kind of olive oil is for you, and anoint yourself with it, for it is a great help with piles." Ibn al-Juzi has transmitted this hadith.

It is a tradition that shaytan does not approach anyone who anoints himself with olive oil. Indeed the Prophet, may Allah bless him and grant him peace, used to recommend olives and saffron in cases of pleurisy, and he used to say that olives are the medicine of the poor.

The green olive is cold and dry, and very nourishing. It fortifies the stomach, stimulates sexual activity, and counteracts the effects of vapours.

The black olive is hot and dry. It generates spleen and is bad for the stomach.

Salty olives are good for burns caused by fire. Chewing the leaves from an olive tree is very good for thrush, rodent ulcers, herpetic eruptions, and urticaria.

Sin

Sabastan – Sebestens

Sebestens is moderate. Gargling with it soothes the throat and stomach. It is used as an ingredient in decoctions, enemas, and other preparations that involve boiling.

Sidr – Lote Tree

Washing with this helps the head more than anything else. It eliminates scurf. The Prophet, may Allah bless him and grant him peace, referred to it in the context of washing the dead. Allah the Almighty also speaks about it:

> ... near the Lote Tree at the Furthest Limit,
> near which is the Garden of Rest,
> when what veiled the Lote Tree veiled it ...

(Qur'an: 53.14-16)

And also:

> ... among thornless lote trees ...

(Qur'an: 56. 28)

Safarjal – Quince

Quince is cold and dry, and very astringent for the stomach. It diminishes the flow in menstruation. Eating quince after a meal relaxes the stomach, but too much of it produces colic. Quince syrup is good for coughs and sore throats. From quince are made an aromatic syrup and a simple syrup, quince purgative syrup, an astringent syrup, quince and lime syrup, and raw quince syrup. Quince ointment invigorates the veins, fortifies the stomach, is a tonic for the heart, and is good for the soul. Quince scented with amber is even more powerful.

There is a well-known hadith which has been related by Anas: "Eat quince on an empty stomach."

Talha said, "The Prophet, may Allah bless him and grant him peace, passed me a single quince and said, "Eat this, for truly it softens the heart." Ibn Maja has transmitted this hadith, and also the following: "The Prophet, may Allah bless him and grant him peace, said, 'Eat quince, for it sweetens the heart, and Allah has not sent any prophet as His messenger without giving him the quince of the Garden to eat, for that quince gives him the strength of at least forty men.'" And from the same source comes this hadith: "Feed quince to your womenfolk when they are pregnant, for it makes the heart tender, and it makes the heart better." By the words 'makes the heart tender' he means that quince imparts excellence and sensitivity to the heart.

Sukar – Sugar

Sugar is hot and wet. It clears out phlegm, and relaxes the stomach. Brown sugar is more soothing. It propels the action of a remedy into the innermost part of an organ.

As for sugar cane, it is excessively wet. It very often generates scabs.

Sakk – Myrobalan

Myrobalan fortifies the stomach and neutralises the smell of sweat.
There is a hadith which has been related by Ibn 'Ali Shabayba that the Prophet, may Allah bless him and grant him peace, found myrobalan very agreeable.

Salwa – Quail

Allah the Almighty says:

... and We sent down manna and salwa for you ...

(Qur'an: 2.57)

The characteristic of quails is that they are hot and dry, although, it is said, not excessively.

Quails come from China. The ones which survive are the white ones, and the ones that do not survive are the green ones. Their medicinal properties depend, to a greater or lesser extent, on which trees they roost in.

Quail meat is good for the chest and beneficial for coughs. It has a cleansing effect.

Quails are birds which come from near the sea, and eating them softens an unfeeling heart. They produce excellent chyme and are equally beneficial for those who are in good health and for those who are convalescing.

The temperature of quail meat is about the same as that of chickens.

Quails are called 'victims of thunder', because if a quail hears thunder, it is liable to die.

Samaq – Sumach

Sumach is cold and dry, and astringent. It stains the stomach, and also stimulates the appetite.

Saman – Ghee (Rancid Butter)

Ghee is hot and wet. It is the most fatty of all seasonings. It harms the stomach. When rancid butter made from cows' milk is mixed with honey, it acts as an antidote to poisons if swallowed.

The Prophet, may Allah bless him and grant him peace, said, "There is healing in cow's milk, and rancid butter made from it is a medicine." There is also a traditional saying that states, "Cows' milk is for you, for it comes from a mixture of all the grasses.

'Ali, may Allah be pleased with him, said, " People will never find anything more excellent than ghee." This hadith has been related by Abu Nu'aim.

Samak – Fish

The best kind of fish is one of medium size, which is found in fresh water, and which feeds off plants rather than mud.

Fresh fish is cold and wet, is difficult to digest, produces phlegm, and balances hot constitutions.

Salted fish is hot and dry, and causes scabs, itching, and piles.

Fishes have many bones.

Jews do not eat fish.

Sanna – Senna

Senna is hot and dry, and in the first degree.

Senna is plentiful in Makka – may this city be exalted by Allah! – and this is why physicians prefer Makkan senna, because it is the best of its kind.

It has been related by Ibn Maja that the Prophet, may Allah bless him and grant him peace, said, "Senna and sanut are for you, for there is a cure in these two for every disease except cancer." This hadith is similar to what the Prophet said about coriander: "In it is a cure for every disease except cancer." This applies to most medicines and remedies.

Among the most excellent of the properties of senna is that it fortifies the heart and induces movement which is not extreme – and it is because of its excellence and many uses that physicians have called it 'the glorious medicine'. It is added to purgative infusions, decoctions, pills, enemas and powders, and it is included because of the beauty of its purgative properties, for it gets bile, spleen and phlegm all flowing, and so its effects on the humours reach the innermost parts of the joints. This is why it is used for pains in the joints and in cases of idiocy. Ibn Sina includes it as one of his cardiac remedies and cordials.

Among the hadith of the Prophet, may Allah bless him and grant him peace, is his question, "What do you use to keep your bowels on the move, and what do you use to encourage a flow from your stomach?" And 'Ayesha, may Allah be pleased with her, replied, "Euphorbia." And he said, "In that there is illness, and it is as hot as fire. Use senna instead." And there is another hadith of the

Prophet, may Allah bless him and grant him peace: "If there is any remedy against death, then it is senna, the gladdening one, the gentle one." The clear meaning and confirmation of these statements has been provided by 'Ali, may Allah be pleased with him, who is our source of information regarding many scientific points. He states that euphorbia is a medicine whose properties are in fact opposed to the active principal that operates in remedies that induce a flow, and that it is hot and dry, and in the fourth degree. Physicians have now stopped using it, because it is dangerous and the flow that it precipitates is extreme.

And as for the word 'sanut', some say that it means 'honey', and some say 'a mixture of Makkan fat'. Others say that it is a seed which is similar to cumin. This is the view of Ibn al-'Arabi. It is said to be the same as Kerman cumin. It is also said to be fennel. Others say that it is something else like this. Still others say that the word means 'dates', while there are even others who say that it means the honey which is stored in leather skins containing fat. Al-Muwaffaq Abdal-Latif agrees with this and maintains that those who make this mixture of fat and honey include ground up senna with it, and that this combination balances the flows and expels catarrh and attracts moisture and oil.

Anas has transmitted the hadith about the Prophet, may Allah bless him and grant him peace, in which he says, "There are three things which are a cure for every disease except cancer. There is senna and there is sanut." And they said, "We know what senna is, but what is 'sanut'?" And he replied, "Insh'Allah you will indeed come to know." And Muhammad added, "I have forgotten what the third thing is."

A drink of a decoction of senna is more efficacious than a drink made from powdered senna. The dose for powdered senna is from one to three drachms, and for the decoction, from seven to ten. If you add violet blossoms and stoned red raisins to a decoction of senna, this is even better.

Sawiq – Flour

A flour which is used a great deal is barley flour. This is colder than wheat flour. It causes wind and is astringent. It can be mixed with honey, and if so, then it is a good food for whoever has a fever. It fortifies the stomach and relieves thirst and sorrow. It is included in some types of pastes.

Siwak – Tooth-stick

This has already been described under the heading of arak, or aloes wood. (See pages 36-37).

Shin

Shatarah – Fumitory

There is heat and dryness in fumitory. Its special property is that it cleanses the blood and makes inflamed humours flow. In the same way, it is good for scabs and itchiness.

Rhazes said, "Fumitory is a solvent which makes inflamed humours flow, and it is also good for scabs and itchiness. The dose for each of these is from four to seven drachms."

I maintain that this is the most efficacious of all purges – but it is essential to add olive oil and sugar.

Shabram – Euphorbia

Euphorbia is hot and dry, and in the fourth degree. It precipitates a flow of phlegm and spleen, since it is swift to take effect and is a solvent. An overdose is fatal, and this is why the Prophet, may Allah bless him and grant him peace, described it as being 'as hot as fire' in the hadith concerning 'Ayesha mentioned above. Accordingly it must not be used until it has been soaked in fresh milk more than once.

The dose is from one qirat to four daniqs, or even less. It is a dangerous remedy, and physicians have stopped using it.

Shaham – Suet

Suet makes whoever eats it hot and wet. When suet is old, its heat is more extreme. Suet from a male animal is far hotter than suet from a female one.

Jews do not eat suet.

Sha'ir – Barley

Barley is cold and dry, and in the first degree. The best barley is white. Barley is not as nutritious as wheat. Barley-water is good for coughs and sore throats. It is a diuretic, it relaxes the stomach, it quenches thirst, and it cools down heat as it dispels it. Barley water is more nutritious than a barley tisane.

Hippocrates said, "Barley water has ten good properties, for it is both sticky and smooth. It is the best food for treating hot diseases."

It has been related by 'Ayesha that whenever anyone in the household of the Prophet, may the blessings and peace of Allah be on him and his family and companions, used to suffer from a painful fever, he would prescribe barley soup, and this would be prepared for them." This hadith comes from Ibn Maja.

Shaljam (also called 'Alift' or 'Lift') – Turnips

Eating turnips regularly is good for the eyesight. A decoction of turnips is good for treating hands and feet which are cold because of cold weather. Eating turnips also increases semen.

Sad

Sabir – Aloes

Aloes is a plant which grows, is cut down, shrinks, and is left until it has dried out. The best aloes come from Socotra, an island off the coast of Yemen.

Aloes are hot and dry, and in the second degree. When mixed with other remedies they neutralise their harmful effects. They also heal swollen eyelids, clear blockages in the liver, drive out jaundice, and gently soothe stomach ulcers.

The hadith has been related by 'Uthman ibn 'Affan, may Allah be pleased with him, that a man once complained to the Prophet, may Allah bless him and grant him peace, about the state of his eyes, during the time when he was doing the pilgrimage. The Prophet said to him, "Cover them with aloes." Salam has also transmitted this hadith. And at-Tirmidhi has written, "Surely there are two commands for effecting a cure: aloes and branding."

Sa'tar – Thyme

Thyme is cold and dry, and in the third degree. It expels wind, removes the causes of flatulence, helps to digest heavy food, beautifies the complexion, increases the flow of urination and menstruation, remedies cold in the stomach and in the liver, and when it is taken as a drink, it kills worms and tapeworms.

Ibn al-Juzi has transmitted this hadith: "They fumigated their houses with thyme and frankincense."

Sandal – Sandal Wood

Sandal wood is cold and dry, and in the second degree. It is good for the eyelids. Sniffing sandal wood, vinegar, and rose water cures headaches. Drinking it fortifies the liver and quenches thirst. It is used in bitter infusions.

The best sandal wood comes from Macassar (in Indonesia).

Sanubar – Fir Tree Seeds

Fir tree seeds are hot and wet. They are heating. They increase semen and desire for sexual intercourse.

Dhad

Dha'in – Sheep

Mutton is more nutritious than goat meat. It is hotter and wetter. I hope to discuss this subject further under the heading of 'Lahm', or meat. (See pages 96 to 99).

Dhabb – Lizard

Lizard flesh is hot and dry. It stimulates the semen.

The Prophet, may Allah bless him and grant him peace, said, "The lizard is not common in the land of my people, and so it does not interest me."

Al-Khalid said, "So they killed it and ate it, while the Prophet, may Allah bless him and grant him peace, watched." This hadith has been transmitted by al-Bukhari and by Muslim.

Ibn 'Umar said, "The Prophet, may Allah bless him and grant him peace, was asked about lizards, and he replied, 'Do not eat it, but also do not make it haram to do so.'"

Jabir said, "The Prophet, may Allah bless him and grant him peace, came across a lizard, but did not eat it, saying, 'I fear that it may be a person who has been transformed into this creature.'"

Dhara' – Udders

Eating the udder of an animal increases the flow of milk in a woman.

Dhari'

This is a bitter, fetid plant.

Allah the Almighty says:

There is no food for them except dhari',
which neither nourishes them nor allays their hunger.

(Qur'an: 88.6-7)

Mujahid said, "Dhari' is the same as the plant known as Shabraq,
which is the same as Sutum."

Dhifdi' – Frogs

Ibn Sina said, "Eating frog flesh makes the body have swelling and
changes its colour. It ruins the semen for ever." Accordingly physicians have stopped using frogs' flesh!

It has already been stated earlier (see page 53) that once a physician suggested it as a medicine for the Prophet, may Allah bless
him and grant him peace, but the Prophet ordered him not to kill
it. This hadith has been transmitted by Abu Daw'ud and by an-
Nasa'i. And from Abu Huraira comes the hadith that the Prophet
forbade the use of all impure medicines, like the lizard and whatever resembles it. Abu Daw'ud has also transmitted this hadith.

Tah

Tabashir – Bamboo Shoots

Bamboo shoots are cold and dry. They strengthen the heart and
remove flux and thirst.

Tahal – Spleen

Spleen is bad meat, for it generates the splenic humour.

The Prophet, may Allah bless him and grant him peace, said,
"There are two kinds of blood which are halal for us – that of the
liver and that of the spleen; and there are two kinds of dead creatures which are halal for us – fish and locusts."

The meat of the spleen is hot and dry. It takes away desire for
food, and it removes desire for sexual intercourse. If it is eaten with
celery, its harmful aspects are neutralised. If it is eaten before taking a medicine, it dulls the sense of taste.

Talh – Bananas

This fruit is also called 'Moz', under which heading it will be described. (See page 105).

Allah the Almighty has mentioned it:

> ... and clusters of bananas ...

> (Qur'an: 56.29)

Tala' – Date Palm Blossom or Spadix

The spadix is the product of the date palm. The sheathe that surrounds the blossom is called 'al-kufra'. Others say that the word 'tala" means the pollen with which the date palm is fertilised.
Allah the Almighty says:

> ... and lofty date palms with clustered fruit ...

> (Qur'an: 50.10)

Talking of palm blossom, Ibn Abdullah said, "I was once walking with the Prophet, may Allah bless him and grant him peace, when we saw some men fertilising the date palms. He asked, 'What are these men doing?' He was told, 'They are taking (pollen) from the male palms and fertilising the female ones (with it).' He said, 'I do not think this is of any use.' The men came to hear of his remark, and so they stopped what they were doing. And that year the date palms did not bear any fruit. When the Prophet, may Allah bless him and grant him peace, heard of this, he said, 'I only thought that this was of no use – so continue to do it. Truly, I am only a human being like you, and so my own opinion may be right and it may be wrong. But when I say, "Allah the Almighty says ..." then accept it – for I do not lie about Allah.'"

Al-Baqusi said, "The blossom of the date palm stimulates sexual intercourse. It is said that if a woman inserts some into her vagina before intercourse, then her pregnancy will be easy."

Date palm blossom is cold and wet. It is balanced by dates.

According to one hadith, 'Ali, may Allah be pleased with him, said, "Honour your aunt, the date palm – for it has been created from the same earth from which Adam was created, peace be on him."

The Prophet, may Allah bless him and grant him peace, once said, "Tell me, which of all the trees is most like a Muslim?" And then they suggested various trees of the desert – but he replied, "No, it is the date palm." Al-Bukhari has transmitted this hadith.

Tayn – Clay

Allah the Almighty refers to this when He says:

And surely We have created man from a mixture of clay ...

(Qur'an: 23.12)

There are two main types of clay: whitish clay and reddish Armenian clay. Both can be applied externally to stop bleeding.

Tayyib – Perfume

Perfume will be discussed under the heading of 'Musk'. (See pages 102 to 103).

Arab scent is very powerful and has already been described.

The Prophet, may Allah bless him and grant him peace, said, "There are three things in your world that I enjoy: women, scent, and the coolness of my eye in prayer."

Thah

Thafar – Hoof

Thafar is a hard bone. Its smoke, when burnt, is good for hysteria.

Inserting a piece of this bone into the vagina after the monthly period is good for getting pregnant.

Among the sound ahadith is the hadith of Umm 'Attayat: "We were given permission, when we did our ghusl after the monthly period, to use a little costus or thafar."

'Ayn

'Ajwat – Madina Dates

Al-Bukhari has described these as being a miraculous medicine. They have already been described under the heading of 'Tamr', that is, 'dates in general'. (See pages 45 – 46).

'Adas – Lentils

The best lentils are those which take the shortest time to prepare for eating. All lentils contain coldness and dryness. Eating them weakens the eyesight. They are bad for the stomach and produce wind. Lentils soaked in water are good for treating small-pox. They are balanced by their being cooked with beetroot. Their opposites are sumach, olives, and coriander.

There is a hadith that says that eating lentils fills the heart with sympathy, and puts tears in the eyes, and takes away pride." This hadith has been transmitted by al-Bayhaqi.

'Asal – Honey

Al-Bukhari has classed honey as a medicine.

Allah the Almighty says:

> ... There comes from their bellies a drink of many colours
> in which there is healing for mankind ...
>
> (Qur'an: 16.69)

Abu Sa'id has transmitted the hadith that a certain man came to the Prophet, may Allah bless him and grant him peace, and said, "Truly my brother's stomach is upset." The Prophet replied, "Make him have some honey." So the man's brother went away. Again he came, and said, "I have given it to him to eat, but he is not any better." (He was given the same advice). The same thing happened again twice more. On both the third and fourth occasions, the Prophet, may Allah bless him and grant him peace, said, "Allah is the truth – and the belly of your brother has lied!" So he gave him honey to eat yet again, and then he was cured. Al-Bukhari has also transmitted this story.

Muslim has written, "Truly my brother has nausea in his belly, his digestion is not functioning, his stomach is upset, and his nausea is troubling him." So the words 'the belly of your brother has lied' indicate that it was not sufficient to take honey only once or twice, because that man's diarrhoea was in flux. So the Prophet, may Allah bless him and grant him peace, prescribed more honey for him – for it is in the nature of honey to expel whatever is left of whatever has collected in the stomach and the intestine.

Now there is another cause of diarrhoea, and this is when mucus clings to the bowel and interferes with the process of absorption. This illness is known as 'slippery diarrhoea', and with this illness it is honey that expels the excess moisture, for when honey is eaten, the moisture is driven out and expelled downwards, and so a cure is effected. Thus, (to begin with), after the first or second dose, the diarrhoea appears to grow worse – and yet this is one of the best remedies, especially if the honey is mixed with hot water.

I maintain that the majority of physicians are agreed about this, and this is why they say that the constitution needs to be pushed into having several evacuations in this manner. This is for one particular kind of diarrhoea – and in treating this kind, many physicians make a mistake, because they think, in their ignorance, that the patient needs some medicine to stop the diarrhoea. And so it is, that the more astringent medicine the physician gives him to stop it, the more the patient suffers – until Allah sends him a knowledgeable physician who can cure him!

And this shows that the Prophet was aware of all the diseases and the cures and remedies that are suitable for them, may the blessings of Allah be on him, and on his companions, and on his women-folk, and on his company, and on the people of his household!

Al-Qadi 'Ayyad said, "When he, may Allah bless him and grant him peace, said, 'Allah is the truth – and the belly of your brother has lied!' the Prophet was referring to the words of Allah, **'in which there is healing for mankind'**. And this is what Ibn Mas'ud and Ibn 'Abbas and al-Hassan also say. Some have said that this ayah refers to the Qur'an itself. This was the interpretation of Mujahid. However the sequence of words shows that the actual reference is to honey.

Ibn Maja, in transmitting a well-known hadith from Abu Huraira, said, "Whoever eats honey three times a month will not meet with any great disaster."

The Prophet, may Allah bless him and grant him peace, said, "You have two medicines: honey and the Qur'an." Ibn Maja has also transmitted this hadith.

Jabir said, "I heard the Prophet, may Allah bless him and grant him peace, say, 'If, out of all the remedies that you have, there is any one thing which is better than all the rest, then it is making use of scarification and eating honey.'" This hadith has been transmitted by al-Bukhari and by Muslim.

'Ayesha, may Allah be pleased with her, once remarked, "How the Prophet, may Allah bless him and grant him peace, loved to eat honey!" Another time, 'Ayesha said, "The Prophet, may Allah bless him and grant him peace, did indeed love to eat sweetmeats and honey." Al-Bukhari has recorded these ahadith.

Honey is hot and dry, and in the second degree. The best of all honeys is that which is made in the spring, then the honey of summer, and last of all the honey of winter.

All physicians are in agreement that honey is the best healing for mankind, for it possesses both detergent and tonic properties, and it is the best of foods. It also fortifies the stomach and stimulates the appetite.

Honey is good for the aged, and for those who suffer from phlegm. It relaxes the constitution. It is also good for bites from mad dogs if used as a paste. If, after eating poisonous mushrooms, it is taken with hot water, the sufferer will be cured. Honey preserves the strength of syrups and such like, as is a matter of experience. It also preserves fresh meat for up to three months, and cucumber and cassia for up to six months, which is why it is called 'the powerful preserver'.

If the body is smeared with honey, this kills off lice. It softens the hair, makes it grow longer, and makes it look more beautiful. When honey is used as an eye ointment, it improves the eyesight. When used in a mouth-wash, it protects the health of the gums and whitens the teeth. It is the food of foods, the drink of drinks, and the medicine of medicines.

Sweetmeats and cakes made with honey retain their qualities. Honey attacks bile, but if it is used with vinegar, its harmfulness is neutralised and its advantages are restored. Licking honey on an empty stomach eradicates a depraved appetite and clears blockages of the liver, kidneys and bladder. No better food has ever been created for us.

Abdal-Latif said, "In treating many diseases, honey is better than sugar because it is a laxative, a cleanser, a solvent, a resolvent, and a purifier. In sugar, all these properties are less pronounced. Sugar is more relaxing for the stomach, which is not the case with honey. Sugar is only superior in two respects: It is not so sweet, and it is not so powerful. Certain Andalusian physicians have written a discourse on honey, and have declared that it is preferable to sugar.

The Messenger of Allah, may Allah bless him and grant him peace, used to drink a cup of honey and water on an empty stomach every day. This is a tremendously prudent thing to do to preserve one's health.

The Prophet, may Allah bless him and grant him peace, used to look after his health in many ways. Among them was that he used to drink an infusion made from dried grapes and eat dried dates for his meals. Another was his use of perfumes, ointments and collyriums for his eyes. And another was his habit of going in to his women. How noble his way of life was, and how excellent.

When the Prophet, may Allah bless him and grant him peace, said, "You have two medicines: honey and the Qur'an," he combined together both worldly medicine and divine medicine, the natural element and the spiritual element, remedies for the body and remedies for the soul, earthly principles and heavenly principles. This indeed involves a subtle secret – that a man should not be content with the Qur'an alone and abandon action altogether. No, rather he should behave as he has been commanded to behave, and he should work for his provision each day, in accordance with what has been decreed for him. And at the same time he should both seek the forgiveness of Allah and ask for success in what he does, just like the farmer does – who ploughs the earth and plants his seeds, and then prays to the Creator to keep pestilence away and make the rain fall. After this, he can do nothing except put his trust in Allah, the Glorious, the Mighty, trusting that He will grant what is good for his welfare and withhold whatever is necessary to prevent misfortune.

Some 'ulama' maintain that what the Prophet, may Allah bless him and grant him peace, meant when he said, "You have two medicines: honey and the Qur'an," is that in honey there are two cures – a cure for disease and a cure for misfortune, just as there are two cures in the Qur'an, a cure for barriers caused by doubt and a cure for difficulties.

'Ashaba – Asclepias

This is a species of tree known as 'al-'Ashar', and its derivative is called 'sugar of al-'ashar'.

It helps with dropsy, and is good for the stomach and liver.

'Asfur – Sparrow

Sparrow flesh is hot and dry. It stimulates semen and increases its flow during sexual intercourse.

The Prophet, may Allah bless him and grant him peace, forbade killing sparrows without good reason.

'Aqiq – Cornelian

Aristotle said, "Whoever wears a ring with cornelian set in it protects himself from fear of death; and whoever has a drink while wearing it, will stop bleeding." A traditional saying states: "If you wear a ring with cornelian in it, then you will never experience poverty."

'Anbar – Amber

Amber is hot and dry. It fortifies the heart and brain and sharpens the senses. When cooked with rose oil, it soothes heart pains. Amber has been described as 'the king of perfumes'.

Jabir said, "The sea washed up a huge fish for us – known as 'amber' (meaning a whale from which ambergris comes) – and we fed off it for a fortnight." (See page 38).

'Anaab – Jujubes

The jujube is hot and has some wetness. Drinking it is beneficial for small-pox and measles. It cools down hot blood. It is used in decoctions, infusions, remedies prepared by being boiled, and enemas.

'Anab – Grapes

The best kind of grape is the pale Persian grape, then the red, and then the black.

Grape flesh is hot and wet, while the skin and pips tend to be cold and dry.

Grapes are an excellent food and at their best and most enjoyable when ripe. The best of all are the last to be harvested. However grape juice results in flatulence. Eating too many of them makes one thirsty, which can be remedied by eating bitter pomegranate. If the result is vomiting, then the remedy is sumach seeds.

It has been related in the ahadith that the Prophet, may Allah bless him and grant him peace, loved eating grapes and melons.

'Aud – Aloes Wood

The best aloes wood is called 'Qamari', and the best of this is tinged with blue. Aloes wood is hot and dry. It invigorates the heart and the senses.

'Aud is also known as ''Alut'.

It has been related by Muslim that the Prophet, may Allah bless him and grant him peace, used to burn aloes wood without mixing it with any other wood except camphor.

'Indian 'Aud' is another name for costus.

The Prophet, may Allah bless him and grant him peace, said, "Aloes wood is a cure for seven things. When used as a snuff it is good for treating the disease known as 'al-Ghudrah'. It is also efficacious in treating cases of pleurisy. Al-Bukhari has transmitted this hadith, and insh'Allah I will discuss it further under the letter 'Qaf'. (See page 86).

Aloes wood contains heat, it relieves vomiting, and it is beneficial for phlegm and coughs.

Ghayn

Ghaliya – Civet

Civet soothes headaches, fortifies the heart, and calms palpitations. When used as a pessary, it helps with pregnancy.

The Prophet, may Allah bless him and grant him peace, used to like civet, and he would say, "Do not disregard this."

Ghazal – Gazelle

The flesh of a young gazelle is hot and dry. It is the best game meat and the most delicious. It is a desiccant, although it does not take long to digest.

Ghurab – Crow

There are four main kinds of crow. One is big and black, and another is black and white. They all eat carrion. It is haram to eat their flesh.

The Prophet, may Allah bless him and grant him peace, said, "There are five creatures that may be killed whether you are outside or within the Haram." One of these is the crow. And he also called it a trespasser..

The third kind of crow is the corn crow, which is known as 'al-Zagh'. It only eats corn and has a pleasant sandy colouring.

The fourth kind is called 'al-Ghudaf'. It too has a pleasant sandy colour, and some say that it is edible, while others say it is not.

In fact all crows have bad meat, which is difficult to digest and produces spleen and leprosy. Physicians forbid people to eat them.

Fa'

Faghiya – Henna Blossom

Henna blossom is good for hot swellings. If wrapped in woollen garments it deters moths.

In the *Sh'ab al-Ayman* there is a well-known hadith that has been related by Burayda in which he says that the Prophet, may Allah bless him and grant him peace, said, "The lord of sweet-smelling blossoms in this world and the next is henna blossom."

It has been related by Anas that the Prophet, may Allah bless him and grant him peace, loved sweet-smelling blossoms, especially that of henna. This hadith has been transmitted by al-Bayhaqi.

Fajal – Radishes

The nutritional value of radishes is minor. They contain hotness. They clear blockages in the liver. They assist, ease and facilitate the digestion of other food, but are themselves difficult to digest. Eating radishes encourages lice.

Sa'id ibn al-Massiyib said, "Whoever enjoys eating radishes but is unaware of their smell should remember the Prophet, may Allah bless him and grant him peace, whenever he first nibbles at or eats one."

Fistaq – Pistachio Nuts

The pistachio nut is hot and dry. The outer red skin stops vomiting and diarrhoea. It is said that if a person eats pistachio nut kernels with egg yolk, then it gives him vitality and fortifies his heart.

Fidhdha – Silver

If one eats silver it fortifies the heart. It is good for palpitations. Using containers made of silver is haram.

Faqqa' – Beer

Beer is bad for the stomach and the nerves. It causes wind.

Filfil – Pepper

Pepper is hot and dry, and in the fourth degree. It produces warmth and reduces wind.

Qaf

Qitha – Cucumber

Cucumber is cold and wet, and in the second degree. It is best when ripe. It cools down heat. It is lighter than the type known as 'Khiyar'. (See page 60). It is a diuretic.

The Prophet, may Allah bless him and grant him peace, used to eat cucumber with unripe dates.

'Ayesha, may Allah be pleased with her, said, "My mother treated me with all kinds of things, and yet I did not put on any weight – so I was given cucumber and unripe dates, and then I became as plump as was good for me." Another version of this hadith is as follows: "The Prophet, may Allah bless him and grant him peace, told my parents to give me cucumber and unripe dates to eat, and so I became plump."

This shows that it is permitted to use medicine in order to enable women to gain weight.

Qara' – Pumpkin

Allah the Almighty refers to pumpkins in the story of Yunus, peace be on him, when He says:

And We made a tree of gourds grow above him ...

(Qur'an: 37.146)

The pumpkin is cold and wet, and in the second degree. It generates a balanced humour. It does not take long to eat. It relieves coughs and is the best food for anyone who has a fever.

Muslim has transmitted the hadith that the Prophet, may Allah bless him and grant him peace, was very fond of dried pumpkin. He has also reported that he, may Allah bless him and grant him peace, once said, "Let them have pumpkins, for they stimulate the intellect and the brain." 'Ayesha, may Allah be pleased with her, said, "As for whoever eats pumpkin and lentils together, his heart will diminish and his sexual energy will increase."

If pumpkin is eaten with bitter pomegranates and sumach, then bile is produced.

Qartas – Matting

Al-Muwaffaq Abdal-Latif said, "This is a medicine made from papyrus grass matting. Galen includes it in his list of haemostatics and says that it is good for intestinal ulcers.

Papyrus grass has already been discussed under the letter 'Ba". (See pages 39 to 40).

Qast – Costus

Costus is hot and dry, and in the second degree. It helps with palsy, stimulates the semen, and is an antidote for viper bites. Sniffing it dissolves catarrh, and when used as an ointment it eases lumbago.

The Prophet, may Allah bless him and grant him peace, said, "It is very good to be treated with scarification and costus." Al-Bukhari has transmitted this hadith.

There is a subtle secret in the Prophet's linking scarification and costus together, may Allah bless him and grant him peace, and it is this: If the cuts made by the scalpel in scarification are rubbed with costus, no scars will be left in the skin. This is one of the marvels of medicine. If scarring does occur in the skin, then you will often see them turn into leucoderma and vitiligo. It is natural to dislike such marks, and so wherever this precaution is known, it is prescribed along with scarification – and how very reliable it is!

Costus is also known as 'Indian Aloes'. (See page 83). The Prophet, may Allah bless him and grant him peace, referred to it by this name when he said, "Accept being treated with costus, because it has many advantages." Jabir related the story as follows: "The Prophet, may Allah bless him and grant him peace, entered the tent of 'Ayesha, may Allah be pleased with her, and there was a child with a bleeding nose with her. He said, 'What is this?' and they replied, 'Truly the child has the disease called al-Ghudrah.' And he replied, 'Shame on you – do not murder your children! How many times has this child had al-Ghudrah or pains in the head?' Then he took some Indian costus, and ground it up into a powder, and then put it up the nostrils of the child. And 'Ayesha told them to continue doing the same. And the child was cured. Some people attributed the cure to the benefits of scarification."

The word 'al-Ghudrah' means 'pain in the throat'. The word is also used to describe the coughing up of blood from a person's throat – from the part which physicians call the tonsils – which damages the tissues of the tongue. These organs are situated in the upper part of the throat near the mouth of the wind-pipe. Women call them 'binat al-adhan', meaning 'the daughters of the ears'. They squeeze them with their fingers to make them return to their normal condition. Another hadith states that the Prophet, may Allah bless him and grant him peace, said, "Do not harm your children by lifting the uvula." Abu 'Ubayda said, "The words 'by lifting the uvula' refers to the women's removing this organ with their fingers."

The following hadith has been related by Zaid ibn Arqam: "The Prophet, may Allah bless him and grant him peace, said, "Treat cases of pleurisy with marine costus." Now there are two types of pleurisy: Real pleurisy is a hot swelling affecting the membrane which lines the ribs. Pseudo pleurisy is characterised by a similar pain in the side, but it is caused by compressed wind gathering in the lower region of the peritoneal cavity. This pain is protracted, whereas the pain in real pleurisy is a stabbing pain. The remedy for true pleurisy is described in the section dealing with those who suffer from diarrhoea. (See page 150).

Returning to the use of costus, if it is ground up and mixed with olive oil, and then rubbed over where the pain is, or taken orally, there is nothing that is more beneficial.

Masih said, "Costus strengthens the internal organs and expels wind. It is good in treating cases of pleurisy."

Perhaps I should point out that Masih is one of the most excellent of physicians, and one of the most distinguished. He has written several works on medicine. Ibn al-Baytar refers to him in his *Jami' al-Kabir*.

Qasab – Reed

Among those plants classed as reeds is sugar cane. This is hot and wet, and it is good for coughs. It cleans out wetness, and the bladder, and has many uses.

Ash-Shafi'i said, "There are three things which are a medicine of medicines: grapes, the milk of a she-camel three months after she has given birth, and sugar cane. If this last one does not grow in your country, then I will not stay there!"

It is said that whoever sucks some sugar after his meals will be happy for the whole day.

There is also a Persian variety of cane, which is dry and not much use. The Prophet, may Allah bless him and grant him peace, forbade its use as a tooth-stick – and so did 'Umar, may Allah be pleased with him. A well-known hadith states that whoever uses this cane as a tooth-stick will inherit tooth decay.

Qutun – Cotton

Cotton is hot, and very effective in providing warmth. Clothes made of cotton are warmer to wear than those made of linen. A wine mixture prepared from cotton dissolves any dead flesh in a wound.

Qanbit – Cauliflower

Cauliflower is cold and dry, and dense. It is difficult to digest. Eating it clouds the eyesight.

Kaf

Kafur – Camphor

Allah the Almighty refers to camphor in the surah that begins with the words, **'Has there ever come upon man a time when he was a thing unremembered?'** (Qur'an: 76.1):

> **Surely the righteous will drink from a cup**
> **in which there is a mixture of kafur ...**

> **(Qur'an: 76.5)**

Kahruba – Yellow Amber

Yellow amber is cold and dry. It fortifies the heart. It attracts straws to itself, just as a magnet attracts iron.

Kabath – Aloes Wood Fruit (See also Arak)

Kabath is the name given to the ripe fruit of the arak bush. It is hot and dry. It fortifies the stomach. Its uses are the same as the arak bush itself.

Jabir said, "We were with the Prophet, may Allah bless him and grant him peace, picking aloes fruit, and he said, 'Pick the ones that are dark.'" This is a sound hadith which has been transmitted by Al-Bukhari and by Muslim.

Kabr – Capers

Capers are resolvents and subtilants and have many properties. They are good for the spleen.

Ibn Abbas has related the following hadith: "The Prophet, may Allah bless him and grant him peace, came out to us and said, 'The Fire laughed – and out came truffles, and the Earth laughed – and out came capers.'"

Kabd – Liver

The best liver is chicken's liver, eaten with vinegar and coriander seeds. Whoever has a cold temperament should eat liver with caraway seeds.

It has been related by Ibn 'Umar that the Prophet, may Allah bless him and grant him peace, said, "There are two kinds of blood which are halal for us – that of the liver and that of the spleen; and there are two kinds of dead creatures which are halal for us – fish and locusts."

Kutm – Indigo Leaf

The effects of eating indigo leaves resemble those of eating pepper seeds. They provoke vomiting, but are beneficial in cases of rabies. When mixed with henna and used as a dye, it strengthens the hair. It has already been described under 'Henna'. (See pages 56-57).

Katan – Flax

This makes the coolest clothing, and the least likely to accommodate lice. The smoke from it when burned dissolves catarrh.

Karafs – Parsley

Parsley is hot and dry. It stimulates sexual intercourse, for both men and women. If animals eat it, their offspring are not born stupid and slow. Anyone who fears that he may be stung by a scorpion should eat it, since it clears blockages.

It is traditionally said that whoever eats parsley before going to sleep will have sweet smelling breath and be free from toothache.

Kurrath – Leek

If meat is cooked with leeks, it loses its greasiness, but eating them causes nightmares and weakens the eyesight.

It is traditionally said that eating leeks before going to bed prevents piles. No king will receive a man who has just eaten leeks. This hadith has been related by the author of *Al-Wasila*.

Kara' – Shins

Ox shins yield a liquid that is thick, tasty and beneficial, with very little that is not nutritious. It is beneficial for anyone who is spitting blood or who has a cough.

The Prophet, may Allah bless him and grant him peace, said, "If I was invited to a meal of only shins, I would not refuse it."

Karam – Grape Vine

The uses of the knotty parts, from which its blossoms spring, are similar to those of the date palm. It is traditionally said that the branches of the vine are like those of the date palm, and that the vine is the date palm's sister.

The temperament of the vine is cold and dry. When used in the form of a paste, it is good for hot swellings.

The Prophet, may Allah bless him and grant him peace, said, "None of you should call the grape (al-'anab) the fruit of the vine (al-karam), because the vine is Muslim. So call the grape (al-'anab) the fruit of the branch of the vine (al-hablat), and call all the branches of the vine as a whole the vine (al-karam)."

Kamun – Cumin

Cumin is hot. It relieves colic and expels wind. If it is soaked in vinegar and then eaten, it removes any desire to have clay or soil.

It is traditionally said that nothing enters the stomach without undergoing some change except cumin.

Kama't – Truffles

Truffles are cold and dry. The best kind are shaped like a jug. Physicians agree that truffle soup clears the eyesight.

The Prophet, may Allah bless him and grant him peace, said, "Truffles are the manna of manna, for truffle soup cures eyes that are sick." This hadith has been transmitted by al-Bukhari and Muslim.

The word 'al-kama't' is a collective term. A single truffle is called 'al-kam', although sometimes the word 'al-kama't' is used to mean one truffle. In this case the plural form is 'al-kamwa't'. A truffle is called 'al-kam', from the root K-M-M, which means 'concealed', because it lies hidden in the earth – just in the same way that we say 'kammaha', meaning 'he has concealed it', to indicate someone who has concealed his testimony.

It is traditionally said that truffles are a pox of the earth. They are also called 'daughters of thunder' because they grow more plentifully when there is a lot of thunder in the air.

It is said that the food of the Tribe of Israel when they were in the wilderness was truffles, which took the place of bread for them. They also ate quails with manna. Now this manna was a sweet dew, and so the food that they cooked was made complete for them.

The words of the Prophet, may Allah bless him and grant him peace, 'manna of manna' indicate whatever comes from Allah to His slaves, without their having to toil and labour for it, and without there being any need to plough or water the land – just that, and nothing else.

Abu Huraira said, "I took three, or five, or seven truffles and squeezed out their juice into a cup. I used it to bathe the eyes of a maidservant of mine, and she was cured."

Lam

Liban – Frankincense

'Abd ibn Marwan said, "There are three things that can only be found in the Yemen – and the land of the Yemen is full of them: frankincense, saffron, and striped Yemeni cloth."

Dioscorides said, "The best incense is the masculine, beaded variety, when mixed with the heart of Moroccan pine. The resin does not catch fire, and although the pine gives off smoke, the incense itself burns without any smoke."

Incense is hot, in the second degree, and dry, in the first. It has many uses and rarely causes harm. It relieves stomach pain, expels wind, makes new tissue grow in an ulcer when used as a paste, dries out phlegm if eaten, and brightens the eyesight when used as a collyrium. If chewed with thyme, it helps stammering. When it is eaten, it increases the understanding. Its fumes are beneficial when there is pestilence, for it sweetens the air and fortifies the body's defences. When taken with black olives and pistachio kernels, it makes a good breakfast, although it causes thirst. And when taken with syrup of roses, it is good for all sorts of urinary infections, and for bed-wetting.

The following ahadith about incense are known nowadays: There is an unauthenticated hadith of Anas which says, "Fill your homes with the smoke of frankincense and thyme." Another hadith, which is ascribed to 'Ali, may Allah be pleased with him, goes like this: A certain man complained to him about his own forgetfulness, and he replied, "Use frankincense, for it truly fortifies the heart and drives out forgetfulness." And from Ibn 'Abbas comes this: "If a person takes a mithqal of frankincense and a mithqal of sugar, and powders them together, and swallows seven mouthfuls of it on an empty stomach, then it should benefit any urinary problems, and he will lose his forgetfulness."

A hadith states that the Prophet, may Allah bless him and grant him peace, said, "Feed your womenfolk with incense when they are pregnant, and then surely the child in the womb will turn out to be a man with a strong heart – and should the child turn out to be a girl, then she will have a beautiful figure with wide hips." Abu Nu'aim has transmitted this hadith.

If frankincense is left to soak, and then the water in which it has been soaked is drunk on an empty stomach, this takes away forgetfulness.

Temporary amnesia is usually due to cold. The kind that is due to dryness is recognisable by its being preceded by insomnia. The treatment for this type of forgetfulness involves using remedies that generate wetness.

Forgetfulness is caused by the following things: scarification on the nape of the neck, eating green coriander or sour apples, excess grief, reading epitaphs on tombstones, gazing at stagnant water or urine, using water tainted with urine to do wudu (an action which was forbidden by the Prophet, may Allah bless him and grant him peace), gazing at someone who has been crucified, passing between two camels tied head to tail as they walk along the road, not having lice in your scalp, and, finally, eating food which has been nibbled at by a mouse.

Laban – Milk

Allah the Almighty says – may the One Who says it be glorified for ever:

> ... and rivers of milk whose taste never changes ...

> (Qur'an: 47.15)

And also He says:

> ... pure milk, tasting good to those who drink it.

> (Qur'an: 16.66)

The Prophet, may Allah bless him and grant him peace, said, "Let whoever is given milk by Allah say, 'May the blessing of Allah be in it, and may He give us more of it, for I know that there is no other food or drink that can take its place.'" This hadith has been transmitted by Abu Daw'ud and at-Tirmidhi, on the authority of Ibn Abbas. And from Ibn Abbas there is also the hadith that the Prophet, may Allah bless him and grant him peace, loved milk.

You should know that milk is made up of a mixture of water, fat and cheese. The cheese is cold and wet and makes a solid food. The fat is good for the body. The liquid part is hot and wet and gives energy to the constitution.

Fresh milk is hot and wet, while sour milk is cold and wet. The best kind of fresh milk is human milk, drunk straight from the breast.

Every kind of milk stays fresh for a certain amount of time, and then its taste changes and it goes sour. Thus Allah the Almighty describes the milk of the Garden by saying, 'milk whose taste never changes'. (Qur'an: 47.15).

The milk of any animal whose period of pregnancy is longer than that of a woman is certainly not good for you.

Fresh milk produces chyme. It purifies the body, increases semen, and stimulates sexual intercourse. Milk relaxes the bowels, relieves depression, and stimulates the brain even though it has wind. However, drinking too much milk encourages lice.

When taken with sugar, milk improves the complexion and results in plumpness. It alleviates minor itching and scabies. It also improves the memory. Every kind of milk, except that of a she-camel, is a diuretic – which is why milk is used in treating cases of dropsy.

The following story has been reported by Anas: "The people of 'Akal or 'Arayna were on the move, and when they entered Madina, they were suffering from an illness known as 'al-hawi'. So the Prophet, may Allah bless him and grant him peace, ordered some she-camels for them and told them to drink their milk and their urine. When they were well, they left."

The above hadith has been transmitted by al-Bukhari, Muslim, Abu Daw'ud, at-Tirmidhi, as-Sina'i and Ibn Maja. According to Muslim's account, the number of people who were ill was between three and nine. Other accounts state that it was eight people. Anyway, it should be noted that 'al-hawi' is an illness of the stomach; and further, that "Akal' is the name of the tribe, while "Arayna' is the name of a branch of the Buhayla tribe; and 'a she-camel' means one which is in milk. In the account given by Qatada, from Anas, it is stated that a group from the 'Arayna tribe went to the Prophet, may Allah bless him and grant him peace, and said, "We have infected the town with al-hawi, and our bellies are swollen." That is what the hadith says.

Now it is not the milk itself that cures dropsy. What happens is that an illness due to cold attacks the organs and makes them shrink. One of three types of dropsy then evolves. These three kinds of dropsy are known as anasarca, ascites and tympanites. Milk has a cleansing and relaxing effect on the stomach and results in a diuresis of fluids which is even more effective than that produced by artemisia, reeds, camomile, or any of the other remedies used in treating cases of dropsy.

So this remedy is one of the best there is and is very beneficial. There is no other medicine like it for treating this particular disease. And this disease does not usually occur unless there is something very wrong with the liver. So if a person stops taking food and water, and drinks milk instead, then he will certainly be cured. This has been proved through experience. As for using urine, the best kind of urine is that of the Arabian camel. In the ahadith, there is evidence of the purity of urine, because it does not attack the flesh.

It has been related by Ibn Abbas that the Prophet, may Allah bless him and grant him peace, used to rinse his mouth out after drinking milk, saying that the fat in the milk was bad for those who had a fever or who suffered from headaches. This hadith has been transmitted by al-Bukhari and Muslim. The Prophet confirmed that milk fat is the worst possible thing for those who have fevers or who suffer from headaches, because of the speed with which it is converted into bile. Physicians, too, are agreed that milk should be avoided by whoever has a fever or a headache.

Stale milk is thicker and wetter than fresh milk, and is greasy – with the exception of goats' milk. Some fresh milk, and some stale milk mixed with water, were once brought to the Prophet, may Allah bless him and grant him peace, and he drank the fresh, saying, "In this there is good fortune and safety." Al-Bukhari transmitted this hadith.

Goats' milk is easing when taken in moderation, and relaxes the bowels. It produces wetness, and is beneficial in the treatment of tuberculosis, which is a disease of the chest. Cows' milk comes half way between sheep's milk and goats' milk in terms of its texture and viscosity. It is nutritious and causes plumpness. The

Prophet, may Allah bless him and grant him peace, drew attention to its usefulness when he said, "Drink cows' milk, for it is a healing and fattening remedy." And according to Ibn Mas'ud, he also said, "Allah did not create any disease without also creating a remedy for it – so drink cows' milk, for cows feed off all sorts of plants." This hadith was transmitted by an-Nasa'i. 'Feed' of course means 'eat'.

Now the above hadith teaches us two things: The first is that Allah has not created any illness without also creating a cure for it. It therefore follows that man should make use of his faculties and direct his energy towards learning about medicine – for if he knows that there is the possibility of there being a cure for every disease, and that a remedy exists for every disease, then surely he will want to find out what they are. Indeed taking care of health is one of the most noble of aims, as has already been stated. And it is towards this end that all the requirements of the deen and this world lead.

The second thing that we learn is that our attention is drawn to the many benefits that milk has, for the Prophet, may Allah bless him and grant him peace, said, "So drink cows' milk ...", in order to emphasise, and to encourage us. And this shows that there are various benefits in milk for treating various diseases. However the Prophet was not content with just saying this, but also gave the precise reason why, when he added, "... for cows feed off all sorts of plants." Thus milks differ, depending on the different fodders that the animals eat. A hot pasture results in hot milk, and a cold pasture results in cold milk, and so on. When the Prophet said, "... feeds off all sorts of plants," he implied that there are different kinds of milk for different diseases – and if there are indeed these different kinds of milk, then how true his words are as regards their usefulness in their containing many remedies. How excellent and comforting this command and conclusion are!

She-camel's milk is more shining and less fatty than others, and it is more likely to loosen the bowels. It does not curdle in the stomach. It is very good for whoever suffers from gastritis because of a weak liver.

The Prophet, may Allah bless him and grant him peace, said, "Truly the cure for the gastric upsets in their stomachs is camel's urine and its milk."

One of the peculiar things about camels' milk is the fact that mice do not drink it. It has been related by Abu Huraira that the womenfolk of the Tribe of Israel lost their fear of mice when they learned that if mice come across goats' milk they will drink it, whereas if they come across camels' milk, they will not. The Jews do not eat camels' meat, nor do they drink their milk.

As for acidic milk, it is harmful for a cold stomach, because of its coldness and its dryness. However it is good for a hot stomach, and stimulates hot temperaments to have sexual intercourse.

As for 'biestings' – by which is meant the first milk after the mother has given birth – this makes the body moist and fertile. It does not take long before it changes, and it is balanced by honey.

As for sour milk, the most excellent is that which comes from cows' milk.

Buffaloes' milk contains much hotness. It is said that one of its peculiarities is that no insect will come near it!

Lahm – Meat

Allah the Almighty says:

> **And We provide them with whatever fruit
> and meat that they desire.**
>
> **(Qur'an: 52.22)**

According to Burayda, the best combination with bread, both in this world and in the next, is meat.

And it has been related by Abu Darda that the lord of food, both for the people of this world and for the people of the Garden, is meat.

Ibn Maja and Abu Huraira have related the hadith that the Prophet, may Allah bless him and grant him peace, once said, "The heart rejoices in eating meat." And 'Ali, may Allah be pleased with him, once said, "Have meat and eat it, because it beautifies the features and clears the complexion." Another saying of Ali's is also quoted: "Meat comes from meat: whoever does not eat meat for forty days in a row will waste away." Another hadith also states that whoever eats meat for forty days in a row will have his heart grow hard. It has therefore been recommended to eat meat on alternate days throughout the year, and to avoid it on the other days. I think that this advice comes from 'Umar, may Allah be pleased with him.

Physicians say that meat is the most nutritious of foods, making the body grow fruitful and strong.

The most appetising of all meats is mutton, which is hot and wet. The best of it is that of the yearling. The meat from an old or emaciated animal is bad for you. Dark meat is the least heavy. The meat of a male animal is excellent, and the best of that is the hind and fore quarters.

Among the sound ahadith on the subject are the following:

A shoulder of mutton was presented to the Prophet, may Allah bless him and grant him peace, and he used to like this part of the animal.

Ibn 'Abbas said, "The Prophet, may Allah bless him and grant him peace, used to enjoy meat, and I used to bring him the shoulder and what was next to it." A similar hadith has been related by Abu Huraira.

It has been related by Mujahid that in the eyes of the Prophet, may Allah bless him and grant him peace, the best part of a she-goat was the fore quarters. It is said that the worst part of the animal is its head and entrails. The meat from the neck is delicious and easily digested.

Another hadith states that in the opinion of the Prophet, may Allah bless him and grant him peace, the breast of a she-goat and what is next to it are the best parts, and the least likely to be harmful. This hadith has been related by Abu 'Ubayda.

The meat from the back is good food, and helps to produce healthy blood. According to a hadith transmitted by Ibn Maja, the best meat in the eyes of the Prophet, may Allah bless him and grant him peace, was the meat from the back.

Roast meat is the driest, and boiled meat is the wettest.

Galen, who was the 'mother' of the art of medicine, said, "The best meat is boiled meat. Fat and suet are bad for you, and contain only a little nourishment. Meat from the right side is lighter and better than that from the left."

The Prophet, may Allah bless him and grant him peace, said, "Chew your meat well, because then it is more easily digested and more nutritious." In another version of the same hadith he, may Allah bless him and grant him peace, is said to have said, "... because then it is more enjoyable and more nutritious." Abu Daw'ud has transmitted this hadith.

Abu Daw'ud also verified the account that the Prophet, may Allah bless him and grant him peace, once ate some of the shoulder of a she-goat and then stood up to pray without doing wudu.

Nafi' said, "'Abdullah sometimes used to go without meat for a whole month, but during the month of Ramadan, he would never deny himself it."

Muhammad ibn Wasa' said, "Eat meat, for it improves the eyesight." Az-Zuhri said, "Eat meat, for it multiplies your strength seventy times over."

Goat flesh is at its best when the animal is two years old. At that point it only has a little hotness in it, and it is dry. It generates excellent humours. Goat flesh is at its worst when it is exceedingly dry, because then it is difficult to digest, and it generates spleen. They also say that it results in an anxious mind and forgetfulness. The meat from a she-goat is better than that from a male.

The Prophet, may Allah bless him and grant him peace, said, "Be kind to goats and leave them alone, for the goat is indeed one of the animals of the Garden." This hadith has been transmitted by an-Nasa'i.

The flesh of a kid is evenly balanced, especially that of a suckling kid. It is easily digested, and there is a minimum of waste.

Beef tends to be cold and dry, and it is difficult to digest. It generates spleen. It is better when eaten in the form of veal.

It is from Suhib that the statement, "Drink cows' milk, for it is a healing ..." comes.

Beef fat is a medicine. It is best eaten with pepper and cinnamon.

Horse meat is hot, dry, heavy, and harmful. Whether or not it can be treated as food is disputed. However, it is correct to state that on the day of the battle of Khaybar, the Prophet, may Allah bless him and grant him peace, made it haram to eat the meat of a domestic ass, but permitted horse flesh to be eaten.

Camel flesh is hot and dry, and generates spleen. The meat from a young camel is best. Camel meat is fatty, greasy and smelly. Ibn Sina says that the meat of camels, horses and asses are the worst of all the meats. Indeed the Prophet, may Allah bless him and grant him peace, made it obligatory for anyone who eats the meat of a wild ass to do wudu. He also forbade eating the flesh of beasts of prey which have canine teeth, and of birds that have curved talons.

As for the flesh of birds, the less that is eaten the better, for it results in fevers.

There is a hadith that says that the Prophet, may Allah bless him and grant him peace, said, "O people, as for meat, it is as addictive as wine is addictive." This hadith has been reported by al-Malik in his book called *Al-Muwatta'*, which means '*The Well-Trodden Path*.'

Lisan al-Asfur – Ash Tree Seeds

These seeds contain hotness. They fortify the heart, calm palpitations, and soothe pains in the main organs. They are also included in the ingredients of certain decoctions and infusions.

Lisan al-Haml – Plantains

The plantain is cold and dry. It helps to stop bleeding. A syrup is made from it.

Luft – Turnips

Turnips have already been discussed under 'Shaljam', under the letter 'Shin'. (See page 73).

Loz – Almonds

Sweet almonds alleviate coughs, giving them moisture. Bitter almonds are hot and help to dissolve stones.

The following has been related from 'Ayesha, may Allah be pleased with her: The Prophet, may Allah bless him and grant him peace, was brought a dish of barley and almonds, but he refused it, saying, "This is the food of tyrants and of those who will come after me."

Lu'lu' – Pearls

Pearls are evenly balanced between hot and cold, and between dry and wet.

They are beneficial in treating palpitations, fright and fear. A collyrium made from them dries up moisture in the eyes. Sucking pearls fortifies the heart.

Allah the Almighty refers to them:

From both of them come pearls and coral.

(Qur'an: 55.22)

Limun – Limes

The peel and the seeds of limes are hot and dry, but the leaf is cold. When mixed with sugar, limes protect health, reduce phlegm, destroy bile and increase the appetite. Drinking lime juice helps to stop vomiting and nausea.

Mim

Ma' – Water

They say that the Prophet, may Allah bless him and grant him peace, said, "The best drink, in this world and in the next, is water."

Water is wet and cold. It extinguishes heat and maintains the natural wetness of the body. It combines with food and facilitates its entry into the veins. The perfection of food is only made complete by it.

The best water is flowing water, heading east, and open to the air. The next best one is that which flows north. Water that passes over soil is better than that which passes over stones. Flowing water is the best of all. The quality of water is known through its purity, the absence of smell and taste, by its clarity, by its distance from its source, and by its depth. The water of the Nile possesses most of these qualities.

Ibn Sina said, "The water of the Nile is highly renowned for four reasons: its great distance from its source, the excellence of its river bed, the fact that it flows towards the north, and its great volume." In those times it was the best water. The water of the Euphrates is similar to it.

The Prophet, may Allah bless him and grant him peace, said, "The rivers known as the Saihan (Syr Darya), the Jaihan (Amu Darya), the Nile, and the Euphrates, are among the rivers of the Garden."

Hippocrates, who was the teacher of Galen and a master of all the sciences, said, "Avoid drinking either when the stomach is completely full, or when it is completely empty – except out of necessity."

Water that has been left standing overnight is excellent because it is free from mud particles and such like. When the Prophet, may Allah bless him and grant him peace, was offered water to drink, he used to choose the water that had been left standing for some time. Jabir said, "Once the Prophet, may Allah bless him and grant him peace, was thirsty, and he said, 'If you have any water that has been left standing in a leather or earthenware container, I will drink that, but if not, then I will drink direct.'" Al-Bukhari has reported this hadith.

The Prophet, may Allah bless him and grant him peace, said, "Cover over your containers and fasten up your water-skins, for every year there is a night during which a pestilence descends from the heavens, and if it comes down on an uncovered container, or an unfastened water-skin, then some of that pestilence is sure to fall into it." This hadith has been transmitted by Muslim. Al-Laythi al-'Ajami said, "Amongst us, they guard against that night in the year especially during the month of December." Muslim has reported this hadith too.

Truly, you should avoid very cold water, for it harms a person and results in hoarseness and a cough. Constant use of very cold water leads to bloody eruptions, catarrh, and chest pains. On the other hand, however, it is good for counteracting vapours that rise to the head, and it extinguishes the heat of burning fevers. Insh'Allah this subject will be discussed in more detail in the section called 'Treating Fevers with Cold Water'. (See pages 144-145).

Very hot water quietens sexual desires, relaxes the stomach, and slows down and interrupts the digestion – while also being good for the elderly and those afflicted with a cold epilepsy and headaches.

Ibn 'Abbas said, "Whoever washes with water that has been heated by the sun, and then develops white leprous patches, has only himself to blame." Those who have knowledge concerning the ahadith of the Prophet, may Allah bless him and grant him peace, state that this hadith is not corroborated.

Rain water is the best water, and the most subtle. It is good for many diseases because it is light and it has blessing – for Allah Himself says:

And We have sent down from the sky blessed water ...

(Qur'an: 50.9)

Water which runs underground, or through grass, is bad for you. Well water is only slightly subtle. Stagnant water is the worst of all.

The very best water is the water of Zamzam. According to the Prophet, may Allah bless him and grant him peace, the water of Zamzam is a water for drinking. It has the best taste and cures sickness. Al-Bukhari and Muslim have transmitted this hadith.

Finally, well water and piped water are – since they are not exposed to the sun and the air – heavy and not nice, because they are, as it were, confined or imprisoned. However the worst kind of water is the water that flows through lead, or through ice, for the coldness of both of these has the properties of smoky heat.

Mash – Beans

Beans are cold and wet. Their temperament is beneficial. They are good for coughs. They are considered as being one of the excellent foods.

Ma'l-Ward – Rose Water

The rose water from Nisibis is cold. It is good for palpitations and relieves hot headaches. Ten drachms of it, by weight, are enough to sprinkle over ten gatherings. If, however, it is sprinkled on the head, it makes hair turn grey more quickly.

We have already quoted the hadith of the Prophet, may Allah bless him and grant him peace, that perfume should never be refused, and that he himself loved perfume.

Mahmuda – Scammony

Scammony is hot and dry, and in the third degree. It provokes a flow of bile. It retains this property for up to thirty or forty years.

Marjan – Coral

Allah the Almighty says that the best coral is red coral. It is cold and dry. It has a strong effect on the heart, it is good for calming palpitations, and it expels wind.

[Note: The Qur'an does not actually say that the best coral is red coral, but coral is mentioned along with rubies, which are red – '... like coral and rubies ...' (Qur'an: 55.58) – and this may have influenced as-Suyuti's statement. Allah knows best.]

Marzanjush – Sweet Marjoram

Sweet marjoram is hot and dry. It frees blockages in the brain, and it dissolves catarrh.

Anas said, "The Prophet, may Allah bless him and grant him peace, once said, 'May you have sweet marjoram, for it is most excellent for a loss of sense of smell.'"

Misk – Musk

Allah the Almighty says:

... sealed with musk ...

(Qur'an: 83.26)

Musk is hot and dry. It fortifies the heart. Musk is the noblest of perfumes. It is excellent for cold temperaments. It strengthens the internal organs when taken in the form of a drink, and when it is sniffed it is excellent for treating fainting attacks and palpitations. It expels wind and counteracts the effects of poisons.

The Prophet, may Allah bless him and grant him peace, used to perfume himself with this scent. 'Ayesha, too, may Allah be pleased with her, used to perfume him with it before he went into ihram, and again, when he came out of it.

Abu Sa'id has related a hadith, which is not corroborated, which says: "Musk is the best perfume." Muslim has transmitted this hadith.

When women have finished their period, they use musk to repel the after effects of the blood.

It has been related that the Prophet, may Allah bless him and grant him peace, used to ask for this perfume on Fridays; and he said it should be used after having a ghusl with warm water on Fridays.

There is an element in musk that purifies the essential composition of air, especially during times when there is pestilence.

It is halal to use musk as a medicine.

Musk comes from the navel of a wild animal which resembles a deer, but which has two curved canine teeth which look like horns. The best musk deer are found in Khorasan. The next best come from China, and after that, from India.

Mishmish – Apricots

The apricot is cold and wet. It goes rotten very quickly. Dried apricots soaked in water relieve thirst. They are the most beneficial of all plums for the stomach. They are used after first being dried, and then soaked in water.

Mastaki – Mastic

Mastic is hot and dry. It keeps phlegm on the move, fortifies the stomach, arouses sexual desire, sets the bowels in motion, and beautifies the complexion. If it is chewed before taking medicine, it prevents vomiting. If it is mixed with oil of roses, it soothes deep stomach pain.

Maghafir

This is a substance which resembles honey, like manna and gum. People prepare it for eating by grinding it with stones. It comes from a tree called 'Ramas', and also from a tree called "Ashar'. The gum which comes from the 'ashar tree is called 'sugar of 'ashar'.

Maghafir is referred to in the ahadith. In this book, 'ashar has been described under the letter "Ayn'. (See page 81).

Massalah Milah – Purified Salt

Purified salt is hot and dry, and in the third degree. When used in moderation it beautifies the colour of the skin. It makes things flow, can provoke vomiting, and stimulates the appetite. When used excessively it causes itchiness.

It has been related in a hadith that the Prophet, may Allah bless him and grant him peace, said, "The lord of your food is salt." This hadith has been transmitted by Ibn Maja.

It has been related by Ibn Mas'ud that the Prophet, may Allah bless him and grant him peace, was doing the prayer once, and while he was in sajda, a scorpion stung him on the finger and then scurried away. The Prophet said, "May the curse of Allah be on the scorpion, which has no respect for the prophets, nor anyone else." He was then treated with draughts of salt and water, and they soaked the place where he had been stung in salt and water. Then they recited Surat'al-Ikhlas (Qur'an: 112) and the last two Surahs (Qur'an: 113 and 114), until the swelling went away. This account has been transmitted by Ibn 'Ali Shayba. At the very least, it demonstrates the benefits of using salt in treating stings from scorpions and other creatures.

Ibn Sina said, "Truly salt should be mixed into a paste with linseed in order to counteract scorpion poison, for this is an antidote for both hot and cold poisons. It draws the poison out, and then dissolves it.

And from Abu Amama comes this hadith, which is not corroborated: "If anyone says, 'May the praise of Allah be on Nuh in both worlds,' in the evening, then no scorpion will sting him during that night." The hadith which has been related by Abu Huraira is well known, and has been transmitted by Muslim: "If, at evening time, you say, 'I seek refuge at evening time in the perfect words of Allah from the evil which You have created,' then no harm will come to you."

Salt preserves meat and stops it from going rotten or smelly. Salt purifies food, and it purifies solids, even to the extent of purifying gold and silver – for it turns gold yellow, and silver white.

In the *Ma'alim al-Tazayyal* there is the following hadith, which quotes 'Umar, may Allah be pleased with him: "Truly Allah has sent down four great blessings from heaven: iron, fire, water, and salt."

Moz – Bananas

Bananas are hot and wet, and in the first degree. Their nutritional value is minor. People who have a cold temperament eat them with honey.

Some people say that the word 'talah' also means 'banana', but to be precise, it refers to the fruit of the palm tree.

Nun

Narjil – Coconut

This is also called 'Juz al-Hind'. It is hot and wet. The best type, which is white, increases sexual potency and relieves back pain.

Nabaq – Jujube

This is the fruit of the Sidr, or Lote tree. It resembles a medlar.

The jujube is cold and dry. It regulates the temperament, and tans the stomach.

In Abu Nu'aim's book on Medicine, he quotes the well-known hadith that when Adam was sent down to Earth, the first fruit that he ate was a jujube.

Nakhala – Wheat Bran

Wheat is hot when cooked. It is good for chests and coughs. When mixed with radish leaves, it soothes the pain caused by scorpion stings.

Nakhal – Date Palm (See also: Tala')

Allah the Almighty refers to this tree:

... in which there is fruit, and date palms, and pomegranates ...

(Qur'an: 55.68)

The leaves of the palm tree are drying and dehydrating.

Naranj – Orange

Smelling the scent of oranges fortifies the heart, and drinking one mithqal of the peel is beneficial when treating cases of scorpion sting, and stings from other creatures.

The juice benefits inflammation of the stomach, and drives out ticks from the hair.

The temperaments of the peel, the pips and the juice are all the same as the temperament of the orange itself.

If the peel is boiled in olive oil, the mixture helps to remedy scaly legs and hair loss.

Nar – Fire

Allah the Almighty describes the Fire:

> ... and they said, 'Do not go out into the heat.'
> Say: 'The fire of Hell is far hotter!'
> – if they only understood.

> **(Qur'an: 9.81)**

Fire is hot and dry, and at the extreme limit in the fourth degree. It is beneficial in treating all chronic diseases, for cautery is of use in treating them. This will be discussed later, insh'Allah. (See pages 152 to 154).

Narjis – Narcissus

The narcissus is hot and dry. Sniffing it helps clear blockages in the brain, and benefits epilepsy. Its root causes vomiting.

A hadith, which is uncorroborated, states: "You should take narcissus bulbs, for the seeds of madness, leprosy and vitiligo are in the heart, and nothing can destroy them except narcissus bulbs."

N'ana' – Mint

Mint is hot and dry. It is the most subtle of all pot herbs. It fortifies the stomach, stops hiccups, helps sexual intercourse, and if it is put in milk, it stops it from turning into cheese.

Nura – Lime Depilatory

Lime depilatory is made from the paste, which is used for splinting, mixed with arsenic. A third of the arsenic is mixed with water and then placed in the sun, or in a hot bath. When it turns blue, it should quickly be smeared on and then washed off again.

It has been related by Umm Salama, may Allah be pleased with her, that when the Prophet, may Allah bless him and grant him peace, used a depilatory, he would begin with his private parts. This hadith has been transmitted by Ibn Maja. Abu Musa has related a hadith, which is uncorroborated, that a lime depilatory used to be prepared for Sulayman, the son of Daw'ud, peace be on them, before he had a bath.

The area on which the depilatory has been used should be covered with henna. It is also said that using henna after using a depilatory guards against blotches caused by leprosy.

It is stated in the ahadith that the Prophet, may Allah bless him and grant him peace, used to use a lime depilatory regularly, and that he once said, "You should use it too."

The sting of a depilatory can be soothed by using either earth, vinegar, or rose water.

Nufar – Water Lily

The water lily is cold and wet. It induces sleep and soothes headaches. Sniffing it excessively makes the brain drowsy, thickens semen, and reduces desire for sexual intercourse. A draught of it, provided that it is quite pure, helps to alleviate coughs and is not converted into bile.

Namam – Wild Thyme

Wild thyme is hot and dry. It is good for hiccups caused by eating too much.

Namal – Ants

Allah the Almighty refers to ants when He says:

> ... an ant exclaimed, 'O ants, go into your dwellings,
> lest Sulayman and his armies crush you without realising it!'

(Qur'an: 27.18)

If ants are mashed up and applied above the eyes, they restrict the growth of hair; and if ants are put on a patch of vitiligo, it will go.

Hah

Hudhud – Hoopoe

It has been written in a book called *Kitab al-Khwas* that one of the properties of this bird is that if it is tied to someone who is forgetful, then he will remember what he has forgotten. If a man carries one of these birds around with him, he will surely conquer his enemy. If someone – who has been enchanted or put under a spell by a witch – sniffs one, then he will be freed. Its flesh, when cooked, is good for people. However, I maintain that most of what has been attributed to it is not true.

Allah the Almighty speaks about this bird:

**And he looked among the birds, and said,
'Why do I not see the hoopoe, or is he not here?'**

(Qur'an: 27.20)

Halyun – Asparagus

Asparagus is hot and wet. It frees blockages in the kidneys, helps back pain, increases semen, and makes labour easier for women. It is said that if dogs eat food containing asparagus, it will kill them.

Hallilaj – Myrobalan

There are three types of myrobalan: yellow, chebulic (from Afghanistan), and Indian. Other varieties are classified as being one of these.

Myrobalan is cold and dry. When used in the form of a decoction or an infusion, yellow myrobalan provokes a flow of bile, chebulic of phlegm, and Indian of spleen. The seeds are made into syrups, and the yellow seeds cool down a hot mouth. When chebulic myrobalan is mixed with honey and made into a syrup, it increases the semen, and accelerates the appearance of white hair. It is good for the elderly, and stimulates sexual energy.

It is traditionally said that the myrobalan is one of the trees of the Garden. It contains the cure for seventy diseases.

Hindiba – Endive

The temperament of the endive changes with the seasons. In summer it is hot, in winter cold. Its potency fades to nothing at the end of each season. It prevents both hot and cold diseases of the liver. It makes flatulence caused by vinegar or sugar disappear. It is used in decoctions and in dodder syrup.

There is a traditional saying which states, "Eat endives and do not belch, for there is not a single day in which some of the drops of the water of the Garden do not fall on them." This is what Abu Nu'aim says.

Waw

Ward – Roses

Roses are cold and dry, and in the second degree. A hot confection made from them fortifies the stomach and helps the digestion. Whatever the temperament of the brain, heat prevails. Even smelling roses will make a man sneeze. Whoever suffers from such sneezing is said to be suffering from an allergy.

It is from roses that the rose water of Nisibis comes, and from this comes the syrup of roses of Nisibis.

As for the elegant red rose, it is an astringent, and the syrup of roses of Otto is made from it. Simple rose syrup is made from white roses, and this is evenly balanced between being an astringent and a lenitive.

Ointment of olive oil and roses, and ointment of sesame oil and roses, are both made from the hedge-rose. The former mainly fortifies the organs, while the latter relieves pain. You should know this much.

Waras – Pseudo Saffron

Pseudo saffron is hot and dry, and in the second degree. The best of all is the red variety which grows in the Yemen.

When used in the form of an ointment, it is useful in treating chloasma, itchiness, and fissures. When taken as a drink, it is good for treating leprosy. It is good for dyeing cloaks. It also strengthens sexual intercourse.

At-Tirmidhi said, "The Prophet, may Allah bless him and grant him peace, used to recommend olive oil and pseudo saffron as a remedy for pleurisy."

And from Umm Salama comes this: "One of us used to anoint her face with pseudo saffron to prevent chloasma."

The following hadith has been related by al-Bukhari: "The Prophet, may Allah bless him and grant him peace, forbade wearing a cloak dyed with either real or pseudo saffron during the month of the pilgrimage, saying that a dyed cloak invites sexual intercourse, and sexual intercourse is forbidden during the pilgrimage.

Washma – Indigo Plant Leaf

It is called 'washma' because the leaf removes 'al-washama' from grey hairs, that is, dullness and lack of lustre, when applied to the head as a dye.

It has been related by Ibn 'Abbas that a man with his hair dyed with henna walked past the Prophet, may Allah bless him and grant him peace. The Prophet said, "How good that is." Then another man passed by, whose hair was dyed with henna and indigo. The Prophet said, "That is even better." Then yet another man passed by, and his hair was dyed with a yellow dye. And the Prophet said, "This man is the best of all." This hadith has been transmitted by Abu Daw'ud.

Ibn Sirin said, "Ibn Ziyad brought the head of al-Hassan into the tent, and it looked just like the head of the Prophet, may the blessings and peace of Allah be on him and his family, dyed with indigo."

It has been related that the Prophet, may Allah bless him and grant him peace, said about the grey hair of Abu Qahafa, "Change its colour – and by that you will avoid feeling sad."

Ya'

Yaqut – Rubies

Rubies fortify the heart and fill it with joy. They are also used as antidotes. If a ruby is kept in the mouth, it prevents thirst. They do not burn and can not be crushed easily.

Allah the Almighty refers to them:

'... like coral and rubies ...'

(Qur'an: 55.58)

Yasmin – Jasmine

Jasmine is cold and dry. It is beneficial for the elderly, but sniffing it too much turns the complexion yellow. Jasmine oil is heating. If jasmine is dried, made into a powder, and then placed on something, then whatever is black turns white.

Yaqtin – Gourd

This has been described under 'Qara''. (See page 85).

So then, mankind, remember, consider, understand and profit from the words of Allah:

Have they not seen the earth,
how many kinds of every fruitful thing
We have made to grow there?
Surely in that there is a sign,
and yet most of them do not believe.

(Qur'an: 26.7-8)

So say, 'Praise belongs to Allah, the sovereign Lord, the manifest Truth,' Who through His commands has made things which are beneficial and things which are harmful, and Who has taught whomever of His worshippers that He wishes, what the good things are and what the bad things are, and what the temperaments of things are, whether they are hot or cold, or wet or dry.

And all that I have said is just a drop in the ocean, a speck of everything.

And no one remembers except whomever Allah gives remembrance, and as He says:

Surely in this there is truly a reminder for anyone
who has a heart, or who opens his ears and who sees.

(Qur'an: 50.37)

Compound Remedies

Physicians say that they prefer using simple rather than compound remedies, if they find that this is enough. So they make use of compound remedies either in order to influence the properties of simple remedies, or to dispel their unpleasant taste, or to make them more potent. For example, they mix ginger with turpeth to make the latter taste more pleasant, or they mix wax with verdigris oil to increase its strength, or they mix tragacanth gum with scammony to counteract the harmful side-effects of the latter, or they mix opium with the great electuary so that the potency of the medicine is preserved for a long time. Sometimes, if a remedy acts swiftly, something is added to slow it down, or if it acts slowly, something is added to speed it up.

Again, if a disease is a compound disease, then the remedy for it must also be a compound one.

Or, if the intensity of the disease and its concentration are un-changing – or if, because of the nature of the humours of the patient's temperament, no single remedy can be found that will counteract all their ill-effects – then it is necessary to look for a compound remedy.

Or, if because of the remoteness of the diseased organ from the stomach, and because the remedy would not otherwise reach it, or else because its potency would have been lost, then a remedy must be compounded in order to make it reach there swiftly – for example, saffron can be combined with camphor or cinnamon with haematite stone.

Or, if because of the character of the diseased organ, a resolvent must be mixed with the remedy in order to preserve its potency – for example, an astringent or a perfume.

Or, finally, if a simple remedy inherently contains something which will harm any organ, then it must be compounded with whatever will neutralise that harmful side-effect.

Now, if you have understood what I have just written, then know also that everything in creation has something good and something bad in it. If the good aspect predominates, then that thing in creation is admirable and beneficial – and vice versa. In all this there is a wisdom which recognises the excellence and might of Allah, and its absolute perfection, which has no equal in creation other than Him. And when His wisdom required that simple remedies needed to be balanced, one by another, then He sent His messengers, may the blessings and peace of Allah be on them – who were bringers of good news and warners – in order to neutralise whatever was harmful in these simple remedies, and to perfect whatever was beneficial in them.

Labid said, "A noble man will not have to blame himself, for human nature is put right by keeping company with the one who puts things right."

This is not the same Labid as the one who said, "Everything is false – except Allah." – About which the Prophet, may Allah bless him and grant him peace, remarked, "The truest words ever spoken by any poet are these words of Labid." This Labid became a Muslim, and his practice of Islam was excellent.

When the messengers were sent to people, in some cases the good overcame the bad, and so they responded to, and obeyed, and accepted, the guidance of Allah. And so they were cured of the disease of ignorance. And so their station became the station of success, and their final place of rest, the Garden of delights. But among them were some who rejected Allah and His mercy, and so what happened to them was that they were removed far from nearness to Him, and when their bodies died, then the Fire became their destination, and Hell their final stopping place. May Allah protect us from this, by His compassion and His generosity.

A poet once said:

> O you who eat whatever you feel like,
> and then curse medicine and doctors,
> you can only reap what you have sown.
> Prepare yourself for the illness that is coming to you!

Al-Jahiz, the poet, said:

> Life will become sweeter if you meet a wise man:
> and only those who have been well taught
> recognise the excellence of knowledge.
> There is no medicine that can cure anyone
> who is sick with greed:
> There is no physician who can heal anyone
> who is sick with ignorance.

The Prophet, may Allah bless him and grant him peace, gave an example of what the above means when he said, "When Allah sent me with guidance and wisdom, I was like a heavy rain that falls on the earth. Whatever part of the earth is good receives the water, and all of that earth sprouts and grows many plants, while other parts retain the water, and Allah gives it blessing, so that people drink from it, and quench their thirst, and irrigate the land with it. And it so happens that another part of the earth does not retain the water, and neither can anything at all grow on it. The first of these comparisons is like those who understand the deen of Allah, and who profit from what Allah has sent through me, and who know and act accordingly. And the second one is like those people who will not raise their heads, nor accept the guidance of Allah with which I was sent."

So, reflect on the words of the Prophet, may Allah bless him and grant him peace, and may Allah have mercy on you.

5

Dosage of Remedies

It has been well established that when a remedy is very heating, or very cooling, or very powerful, then only a small amount should be used. When exactly the opposite is the case, then a large amount should be used. Similarly, if the beneficial effect of a remedy is only slight, then use a large quantity of it – and vice versa. Again, if the organ to be treated is far from the stomach, then use a lot of the remedy, and if it is close by, then only take a little of it. Similarly, if the organ is a weak one, only take a little of the remedy, and if it is a strong one, then the reverse. Again, if the stomach is very full, then use a strong remedy, and if it is not very full, then do the opposite.

If you understand all this, then make sure that all the remedies that you have are fresh and good – and ask Allah for help, saying, "There is no power except from Allah, the Mighty, the Wise" – and after that you can begin your treatment.

6

Observations on Compound Preparations

I have already described the remedies whose uses are well known earlier on in this part of the book, so there is no need to describe their uses in dealing with the treatment of disease again.

So now we will examine sweet ebullients. These are the ebullients made from jujubes, sebestens, fennel, and extract of liquorice. As for the decoctants which are used to purify sweet ebullients, these include parsley seeds, red currants, and coriander seeds. As for sweet infusions, these include dried apricots, jujubes, water lily blossom, and plums.

As for bitter ebullients, add tamarinds and pomegranate seeds.

As for laxative infusions, these include Meccan senna and violet seeds. They can be strengthened by adding ten grains of scammony with a little tragacanth. All of these should be infused with hot water and strained through sugar.

As for decoctions of fruit, the laxative infusions of chebulic and yellow myrobalan should be added. Apricots and sebestens can be substituted. They can be boiled and strengthened with scammony and rhubarb. As for decoctions of cuscuta, decoctions of its fruit, polypody and agaric should be added. As for scammony, Armenian clay and lapis lazuli should be added. If there is any associated pain in the joints, then colchicum, orchids and turpeth should be added. Others add manna, fumitory, and endives, if there is any itchiness or scabbing.

As for rhubarb linctus, this is made from rhubarb and scammony with plum juice. Cassia honey or carob honey may be added to these instead of plum juice.

As for pills, these include purgative pills and turpeth, the myrobalans, and scammony, mixed with water and used as pills the size of small peas. Al-Maruzi once said, "I said to Abu 'Abdullah Ahmad, 'I've got a severe headache, ' and he replied, 'Then set off a flow in your constitution.' He added, 'Truly this has come as a result of the dryness of your constitution.' And a little later, he said, 'I will give you a pill which I will prepare for you.' Then he produced a pill for me and said, 'Take this at night time.' And he said that it was made with yellow and black myrobalan, mastic, and a little aloes wood." And indeed this pill is good for treating headaches.

As for laxative enemas, these include jujube, sebestens, violet blossom, senna, the seeds of both kinds of mallow, cassia, scammony, borax, brown sugar, sesame oil, and beet slices or leaves.

It was the opinion of Imam Ahmad that enemas were to be avoided except when necessary, as is related in the ahadith of Harab. Mujahid, al-Hassan, Taus, and 'Amar are all agreed on this matter. All except one of them wrote, "And yet we do not forbid them." Ibrahim, Abu Ja'far, al-Hukm ibn 'Ayaina, and 'Ata said words to the same effect. Abu 'Abdullah forbade the use of enemas, but later gave permission for them to be used for the purposes of medical treatment. Al-Khalal has transmitted this hadith, and his isnad includes Sa'd ibn Ayman, who said that 'Umar ibn al-Khattab, may Allah be pleased with him, was very indulgent in this respect.

Among his ahadith there is this hadith which was related on the authority of Jabir: "I asked Muhammad ibn 'Ali about enemas, and he said, 'There is no objection to them – they are a medicine, just like other medicines.'" Abu Bakr al-Maruzi said, "I described the advantages of using enemas to Abu 'Abdullah."

As for the point as to whether inserting an enema breaks the fast or not, there is a difference of opinion regarding this matter.

The first to use an enema was a bird which had eaten too many fish. It used its beak. When it felt over-loaded, it took some salty sea water and inserted it into its rectum, and in this way it made itself excrete what was inside. It has already been stated that salt should be included as being one of the laxatives.

Part Three

7

Treating Disease

It has already been stated that the principal aim of medicine is to preserve health, that is, it is to have health present and to prevent its being absent. This indeed is what we have said. And we have also demonstrated that the Prophet, may Allah bless him and grant him peace, permitted the use of remedies in treating people – indeed he recommended it, for it has been related by Jabir that the Prophet said, "For every disease there is a remedy, and when the remedy is made apparent, then the disease is cured by the permission of Allah the Almighty." In saying this, adds Muslim, the Prophet, may Allah bless him and grant him peace, encouraged the use of remedies in treating illness.

This hadith has been related by Abu Huraira: "Allah has not created any disease without also creating a medicine or a remedy for it." And al-Bukhari adds, "And as regards the last word of the hadith, 'Allah has not created any disease without also creating a medicine or a remedy for it,' the medicine is indeed the remedy."

It has been related that Asama ibn Sharik said, "I was with the Prophet, may Allah bless him and grant him peace, when some Arabs approached him and said, 'O Messenger of Allah, give us some medicine.' And he replied, 'Truly the worshippers of Allah will receive medicine, for He has not allowed any disease to exist without having also created a cure for it.'" To this there is only one exception: senile decay.

All four of the major muhadithun have transmitted this hadith, as well as the following: "Accept treatment and use medicines." As for excessive old age, however, senile decay is like an illness, for death follows close behind it.

From Abu Sa'id comes this: "Truly the Prophet, may Allah bless him and grant him peace, said, 'Allah has not created any disease without also creating a cure for it. Whoever knows this, knows it, and whoever is ignorant of this, is ignorant of it – and the only exception to this is death.'"

Abu Huraira said, "The Prophet, may Allah bless him and grant him peace, said, 'He Who has put disease on the earth, has also put its remedy there.'"

Abu Kharama said, "I once said, 'O Messenger of Allah, do you know of any talisman that we can use, or any medicine that we can find, or any righteous act that we can do, that can affect what has been decreed by Allah in any way?' And he replied, 'Only what has been decreed by Allah exists.'" This hadith has been transmitted by at-Tirmidhi, and he has embellished it.

Now it is in man's nature to look after himself. His body has been created from various combinations. Allah the Almighty says:

Surely We have created man from a drop of mingled fluid ...

(Qur'an: 76.2)

Now, these combinations are the humours. Man's well being and protection are dependant on his constitution being properly balanced. And this, in turn, depends on his utilising what is beneficial for him and avoiding what is harmful for him. And this is the principal aim of medicine.

Disease attacks the essential fluids from which man has been created, and makes them start to decay. The art of medicine is to prevent this decay, and to prevent these fluids from rapidly decomposing. Thus we have the well known saying of the Prophet, may Allah bless him and grant him peace, "Like the Tribe of Adam, at whose side there are ninety-nine diseases. If he avoids these, he will lapse into old age, until he dies." This hadith has been transmitted by at-Tirmidhi.

From Ibn Mas'ud we have this version of the hadith: "If a man avoids this one, then that one seizes him, and if he avoids that one, then this one takes him." This is the version which has been reported by al-Bukhari.

Death is indeed inevitable, but the diseases of old age can be treated with medicine. A physician once said, "The body, by its very nature, must end in death – but medicine makes the time spent waiting for it easier to bear."

Medicine protects the health of those who are healthy, and restores it, as far as possible, to those who are sick. This is clear from the hadith of the Prophet, may Allah bless him and grant him peace, "There are two knowledges: the knowledge of the body, and the knowledge of the deen." However this is not in fact a hadith, but a saying of ash-Shafi'. The correct hadith has been transmitted by Muhammad ibn Sahl at-Tusi, who heard it from ar-Rabi', who heard it from the Prophet, may Allah bless him and grant him peace. His comment was: "There are two kinds of men who are indispensable: those who understand the deen, and physicians who understand the body." The Prophet, may Allah bless him and grant him peace, said, "There are three branches of knowledge: reciting the Qur'an correctly, following the sunnah, and fulfilling obligations with justice. Whatever goes beyond these is unnecessary." This is the hadith as transmitted by at-Tirmidhi and Ibn Maja.

Now, medicine is an enduring part of the sunnah, for the Prophet, may Allah bless him and grant him peace, used it, and he made recommendations about it. He also said, "There are five elements that can be recognised in the practice of the Prophets: "Turning to Allah, patience, blood letting, using a tooth-stick, and using perfumes." And truly there are many ahadith concerning this subject. And Allah knows everything.

Making Use of Medicine

There is universal agreement that making use of medicine is halal. Some are of the opinion that it is advisable to use remedies because of the well known hadith of the Prophet, may Allah bless him and grant him peace, "Use medicine." And also because he himself used to take medicine in both health and sickness.

When he, may Allah bless him and grant him peace, was well, he used to have dates, pumpkins and water melons. He would eat sparingly, have a rest after noon, and combine two times of prayer into one. He would also drink an infusion of raisins, or figs, or similar fruits, as has already been described.

As for the times when he was ill, 'Ayesha, may Allah be pleased with her, said, "The Prophet, may Allah bless him and grant him peace, had many illnesses. At such times, several physicians – both Arab and non-Arab – used to come and sit next to him and treat him."

Hisham said, "I once said to 'Ayesha, may Allah be pleased with her, 'I am amazed by your knowledge of medicine and your skill in using it.' And she replied, 'When the Prophet, may Allah bless him and grant him peace, grew old, he would fall ill, and visitors would come and call on him. It is from them that I acquired my skill.'"

Ka'ab said, "Allah said, 'I give health, and I give remedies – so let everyone use medicine.'"

There is indeed a group who are of the opinion that using remedies should be avoided. There is a statement from Ahmad that it is better to avoid them. This reference is to a quotation in *The Ahadith of al-Maruzi*, who said, "It is halal to use medicine, but it is better to avoid using medicine.

The following question – concerning a man who was seriously ill, but who had refused medical assistance – was once put to Ahmad: "Should we feel concerned about him?" And Ahmad replied, "No, for the belief of this man is to believe in reliance on Allah." Similarly, Ishaq asked him whether a sick man should refuse medicine or take it. To this Ahmad replied, "I would be happier if he relied on Allah and refused to take his medicine."

There is support for this in a hadith which has been related by Ibn Abbas: A woman came to the Prophet, may Allah bless him and grant him peace, and said, "O Messenger of Allah, ask Allah to cure me." And he replied, "I will ask Allah, if you want, and He will cure you – but if you are prepared to put up with your illness, you will win the Garden." And the woman exclaimed, "O Messenger of Allah, then no – I will put up with it!" This hadith has been transmitted by al-Bukhari and Muslim.

The Prophet, may Allah bless him and grant him peace, said, "There are seventy thousand who will enter the Garden without having to account for their actions. These are those who never used branding irons, who never resorted to charms, who guarded their eyes and their ears, and who placed their reliance in Allah." Another version of this hadith only refers to those who have used neither branding irons nor charms. This hadith has been transmitted by al-Bukhari.

The author of this book, may Allah have mercy on him, says: The late shaykh, the imam of the 'ulama', 'Ala'ud-Din ibn al-'Atar, once quoted the following words to me: "All Muslims are agreed that there is no obligation to take medicine – but, on the other hand, the hadith from Ahmad, that there is an obligation, was quoted by the late Shaykh al-Islam, Taqi'ad-Din Ahmad ibn Taimiyah, who transmitted the hadith of the Prophet, may Allah bless him and grant him peace, "Use medicine, for it is halal."

There is the following story about Abu Bakr as-Siddiq, may Allah be pleased with him: He was once asked, "Shall we call for a doctor for you?" He replied, "He has already been to see me." And when they asked, "What did he say to you?" he replied, "'**Surely your Lord does whatever He wants.**'" (Qur'an: 11.107).

It was once said to Abu'd-Darda, "What are you complaining about?" He replied, "My wrong actions." And when they asked him, "What do you want?" he replied, "The mercy of my Lord." And when they said, "Shall we call a doctor for you then?" he answered, "It is the doctor Himself Who has made me ill!"

A group of people once went to see their teacher. When they came in, they said, "Shall we call a doctor for you?" and he answered them, "Even with all his knowledge and his remedies, the doctor still cannot prevent what has been decreed for me."

The author of this book, may Allah have mercy on him, observes that true dependence is the heart's relying on Allah. This never contradicts ways and means, and most means are dependant on dependence. So the wise practitioner does what must be done, and then relies on Allah as regards the outcome.

Allah the Almighty says:

... and let them take their precautions and their arms ...

(Qur'an: 4.102)

And the Prophet, may Allah bless him and grant him peace, said, "Trust in Allah – but hobble your camel!" The Prophet also said: "Lock your doors." ... "And as for me, I will hide in the cave for three days." Perhaps the disease will become chronic, and the medicine used for it, an addiction. Perhaps it will help – and then again, perhaps it will not!

On Calling in a Physician

Jabir said, "The Prophet, may Allah bless him and grant him peace, once sent for 'Ali ibn Ka'ab, who lanced a vein for him and then used cautery." This hadith has been transmitted by Muslim.

The following story comes from Abu Huraira: One day, one of the Ansar fell ill, and the Prophet, may Allah bless him and grant him peace, called in two physicians who were in Madina to see him, and said to them, "Cure this man." In another version describing the same incident, it is said that they asked the Prophet, "O Messenger of Allah, is the science of medicine any good?" And he replied, "Yes."

From Hillal ibn Yassaq comes this story: In the time of the Prophet, may Allah bless him and grant him peace, a certain person fell ill. The person who was sick said, "Call a doctor for me!" But they said, "O Messenger of Allah, this man does not need a doctor." And he replied, "Yes, indeed!"

From the same source comes this account: The Prophet, may Allah bless him and grant him peace, visited a man who was sick, and said, "Send me a doctor for him!" And the sick man said, "O Messenger of Allah, is that you saying that?" And he replied, "Yes, indeed it is!"

The above hadith about the Prophet, may Allah bless him and grant him peace, are all related by Abu Nu'aim in his *Kitab at-Tibb an-Nabbawi.*

From Zaid ibn Aslam comes this account: A certain man was wounded and injured, with internal bleeding. The Prophet, may Allah bless him and grant him peace, called two tribesmen of the Bani Anmar and said, "Which of you two is the better doctor?" One of them replied, "Is the science of medicine of some use then?" And the Prophet answered, "He who sent down the disease, also sent down the remedy." This has been transmitted by al-Malik in his book called *Al-Muwatta'.*

The author of this book says: It is advisable to choose someone who knows about medicine and who is skilful in this art – and this is clear from the hadith of the Prophet, may Allah bless him and grant him peace, which has just been quoted: "Which of you two is the better doctor?" And talking along the same lines, Galen said, "An ignorant doctor visits a man who has a fever. He drives out one fever, but lets in two more in it place, thanks to his giving the wrong treatment, his meagre knowledge, and his profound ignorance."

A hadith, which has already been quoted, states that 'Ayesha, may Allah be pleased with her, said, "The Prophet, may Allah bless him and grant him peace, had many illnesses. At such times, several physicians – both Arab and non-Arab – used to come and sit next to him and treat him." That is what the hadith says.

Ahmad said, "It is permissible to take advantage of the advice of a physician who is a dhimmi if he prescribes a remedy which is halal – but his advice should not be followed if he prescribes a medicine which is haram, such as alcohol and things like it. Similarly, do not pay any attention to him if he says you should break a fast, or fast, or do the prayer sitting down, or anything else like this. In such matters you should only pay attention to advice like this when it comes from two trustworthy Muslim physicians."

Ahmad also expressed a further opinion when he said that it is undesirable to use remedies which come in the form of syrups or decoctions, if they have been prescribed by a dhimmi.

Ahmad ibn al-Hassan stated in his *Book of Ahadith* that taking medicine which has been prescribed by an idol worshipper is detestable.

Al-Maruzi said, "Ahmad used to forbid me from buying medicine that had been prescribed for him by a Christian, because he said that it was possible that he might include haram ingredients – meaning things that were poisonous or impure and such like – believing them to be beneficial."

Prescribing Doing Without Food

Doing without food slows down an illness and enables the faculties to drive it out. The Prophet, may Allah bless him and grant him peace, used to give advice to this effect, and he forbade everything that is harmful.

The author of this book says: "I was told by Imam al-Hafidh Jamal ud-Din Abu Hajjaj Yusuf ibn az-Zaki Abd ar-Rahman Yusuf al-Mazani, who said that he was told by Abu al-Ishaq Ibrahim ibn Isma'il ibn Ibrahim al-Qurshi, who said that he was told by Abu Ja'far Muhammad ibn Ahmad ibn Nasr, the pharmacist, who said that he was told by Abu 'Ali al-Hassan ibn Ahmad, the smith, by Abu Mansur Mahmoud ibn Isma'il, the money changer, and by Fatima bint 'Abdullah al-Juzdaniya – and of these the smith said that they were told by Abu Nu'aim Ahmad ibn 'Abdullah al Hafidh, and the money changer said that they were told by Abu al-Hussayn Ahmad ibn Muhammad ibn Fadshah, and Fatima said that they were told by Abu Bakr Muhammad ibn 'Abdullah ibn Zayd – and all of whom said that they were told by Abu'l-Qasim Sulayman ibn Ahmad of Tiberias, who said that he had received the hadith from Sharih ibn al-Na'man, who said that he had received the hadith from Faliyah ibn Sulayman, who received it from Ayyub ibn Abd ar-Rahman ibn 'Abdullah ibn Abi Sa'sa't, who received it from Ya'qub ibn Abi Ya'qub, who received it from Umm al-Manzir Salma bint Qays al-Ansariyya – and truly, she said, "The Prophet, may Allah bless him and grant him peace, entered my tent, and 'Ali, may Allah be pleased with him, came with him, and 'Ali was recovering from some illness at the time, and we had a palm tree nearby, with some date-clusters hanging from it."

She continued her story: "The Prophet, may Allah bless him and grant him peace, stood there eating them, and 'Ali, may Allah be pleased with him, also stood there eating. Then the Prophet said, 'Slowly, slowly, for you are still recovering.'"

Umm al-Manzir continued: "So 'Ali, may Allah be pleased with him, sat down, while the Prophet, may Allah bless him and grant him peace, continued to eat from the tree, and in the mean time I prepared a meal of spinach and barley for them. Then the Prophet said to 'Ali, 'Have some of this, for it will do you more good.'"

This hadith has also been transmitted by Imam Ahmad, who was told it by Sharih ibn al-Na'man, whose isnad we have already stated. At-Tirmidhi, however, said, "We do not recognise the authorities before Faliyah." However, this hadith has also been transmitted by Abu Daw'ud in his *Book on Medicine*.

(The word 'ad-dawal' is the plural of 'ad-daliyah', and means a cluster of dates on a palm bearing fully grown dates which are just beginning to ripen and are now fit for eating.

The word 'an-naqa' means someone who has recovered from his illness, but only recently, and who has not yet been restored to full health.

The words 'hamiyat al-maridh' mean a sick man's doing without food. The word 'himwat' itself actually indicates telling a sick man not to eat food which will cause him harm, and so the use of the word 'maridh', meaning 'sick man', is unnecessary here.).

As-Sahib said, "I came to visit the Prophet one day, may Allah bless him and grant him peace, and he had some bread and dates in front of him. And he said, 'Come in here, and eat.' So I began to eat some dates. And the Prophet said, 'Why are you eating dates while you are suffering from ophthalmia?'" This hadith has been transmitted by al-Hamida.

It has been related by Qatada that the Prophet, may Allah bless him and grant him peace, said, "When Allah loves His slave, then He protects him from this world – just in the same way that each one of you does not stop guarding the sick from food and drink." This hadith has been transmitted by at-Tirmidhi, and another one very similar to it, by al-Juzi.

It has been related about 'Umar, may Allah be pleased with him, that he would prevent the sick from eating, and he would not even let them suck a date stone, so strict was the regime that he imposed.

The physician of the Arabs, al-Harith ibn Kalda, was once asked, "What is the essence of medicine?" And he replied, "Imposing abstinence from food."

When Ka'ab ibn Sa'd was doing the funeral prayer over his brother Shahib, he said, "Sulayma is asking why your body is so dried out – as if a physician had ordered you not to drink anything at all."

Ahmad said, "There is no objection to prescribing abstinence." When Ahmad himself was ill, he would eat only marrows and peas, and vegetarian meals cooked in sesame oil would be prepared for him. Abd ar-Rahman, the physician, used to prescribe the juice of boiled marrow, mixed with sugar, for him to drink. And this was his diet.

In his *Tibb an-Nabbawi*, Abu Nu'aim relates the hadith that the Prophet, may Allah bless him and grant him peace, would never approach any of his wives while she was suffering from ophthalmia, until she had been cured.

Encouragement to Study Medicine

The hadith of the Prophet, may Allah bless him and grant him peace, which states that Allah has not sent down any disease without also sending down the remedy, has already been quoted.

Imam Shaf'i said, "After the science which distinguishes between what is halal and what is haram, I know of no science which is more noble than that of medicine." He was grieved to see how much of this science had been lost by the Muslims. He often used to say, "They have lost a third of human knowledge, and have allowed themselves to be overtaken by the Jews and the Christians." He also used to say, "Truly the People of the Book have overcome us and overtaken us in this supreme art." And Shaf'i, as well as having immense superiority in the science of the shari'ah, and as well as having an unassailable command of the Arabic language, was also a skilled physician.

The author of this book, may Allah have mercy on him, remarks: I once saw our shaykh, Shaykh Ibrahim ar-Rumi, who was extremely skilled in medicine, as were the Shaykh al-Islam, Taqi'ad-Din Ahmad ibn Taimiyah, and Shaykh 'Imad ad-Din al-Wasiti, may Allah have mercy on them.

The author would also like to add that Hippocrates was the master of this art, and the principles that he observed in this art are the correct principles. After him came Galen, who was also a leader in this art. These two were great physicians, and excelled all the others. They say that the tomb of Hippocrates still exists, and is regarded with esteem by the Greeks.

It is traditionally said that Seth was the first to make the knowledge of medicine known, having inherited it from his forefather, Adam, peace be on them. Some say that he received it through experience, and others say through thinking it out. Some say that the people of Egypt invented medicine, while others say that it was the people of India. Some say that medicine is a form of magic, and that the Prophet Idris, peace be on him, and Hermes evolved the twin sciences of philosophy and medicine. However, it is more likely that it was revealed by Allah the Almighty, to His people. This much is certain, that guess-work and experience alone are not sufficient.

According to Ibn 'Abbas, the Prophet, may Allah bless him and grant him peace, once said, "Sulayman was once doing the prayer, when he saw a bush growing in front of him. He asked it what its name and its uses were, and then wrote them down."

And indeed we have seen both humans and some animals using medicines naturally and instinctively. Thus everyone, when hungry, looks for food, and similarly, when thirsty, seeks water. And when a person is afflicted by sorrow, he calms himself down, and vice versa. If a person suffers from indigestion, then he abstains from food. This is what is meant by 'empirical medicine'.

Again, if a snake emerges after winter is over, and finds that its eyesight is poor, it will seek out and eat some fennel – and its eyesight will be strengthened by the herb, and it will see more clearly. Thus physicians recommend using fennel when treating cases of weak sight. Similarly, a bird which feeds off fish will, when constipated, give itself an enema of sea water. We have already mentioned this. And again, if a swallow's chick goes blind, its mother will bring it the plant known as swallow-wort, even from as far away as China, and it will regain its sight.

Again, if a female eagle has difficulty in laying her eggs, her partner will fly to India and fetch a stone which is known as 'katamat', or 'the stone of secrecy'. It is a stone which resembles the badaqa stone. If she refuses it, then a sound of movement is heard within. Then the male bird places it underneath the female, and then the egg will come out.

Again, if a fox is ill in the spring, it will eat grass, which will induce a flow, so that it recovers. A cat, also, will eat it, and this will make it vomit. And it is a well known fact that grass is not the food of either of these two animals. So praise belongs to Him, Who created everything and gave guidance to be followed.

Hasham ibn 'Urwah said, "I never met anyone who knew more about medicine than 'Ayesha, may Allah be pleased with her. I once said to her, 'O my aunty, where did you learn all your medicine?' And she replied, 'I used to listen to people when they prescribed remedies for each other, and I stored up what they said in my memory.'" Talking on the same subject, he said, "I said to 'Ayesha, may Allah be pleased with her, 'I am astonished by your insight into medicine, O Umm al-Mumineen,' and she answered, 'O son of my sister, when the Prophet, may Allah bless him and grant him peace, grew old, he would fall ill. Groups of people used to come and prescribe remedies for him, and it was from them that I learned about medicine.'"

From the same man comes the hadith that 'Ayesha, may Allah be pleased with her, once said, "O son of my sister, whenever any member of my family was ill, the Prophet, may Allah bless him and grant him peace, used to prescribe a remedy for them. So I used to remember it, and then prescribe the same for other people." This hadith has been transmitted by Abu Nu'aim.

In the hadith of the Prophet, may Allah bless him and grant him peace, in which he begins, "Allah has not created any disease without also creating a cure for it ...", the Prophet's words, "Whoever knows this, knows it," refers to the physicians, and when he added, "... and whoever is ignorant of this, is ignorant of it ...", he was referring to the rest of mankind. And Allah knows best.

It has been related by 'Amaru ibn Sha'ib, in a hadith transmitted from his grandfather to his father, that the Prophet, may Allah bless him and grant him peace, said, "Whoever gives medical treatment, but is not recognised as a physician, and who thereby causes death, or anything short of it, will be held responsible for this." This hadith was transmitted by Abu Daw'ud and an-Nasa'i and Ibn Maja.

And from the same source comes the hadith, "Whoever gives medical treatment without having previously studied medicine, must be held responsible for it." Al-Khattabi said, "I can see no objection to the view that if a person giving medical treatment exceeds his limit, and the patient dies as a result, then that person is responsible. And any person who presents himself as having an expertise which he does not in fact possess, has truly exceeded his limit – and it is generally accepted that expiation for the wrong action of a quack can be enforced by the dead person's heirs."

It is accordingly detestable that anyone who has no knowledge of the art of medicine should be called a physician.

This hadith comes from Abu Ramthah: "I entered the tent of the Prophet, may Allah bless him and grant him peace, with my father. My father diagnosed that he had a back infection, so he said, 'Please let me treat this back infection of yours, for I am a physician.' And the Prophet replied, 'You are my friend. Allah is my physician!'" This hadith has been reported in *Shart'al-Sahiha*.

Doctors' Fees

Abu Sa'id said, "Some of the companions of the Prophet, may the blessings and peace of Allah be on him and his family and his companions, went and camped near an Arab village. No one helped them to get down from their camels, nor were they offered a meal. It so happened that one of the men in the village was bitten by a snake. So then the villagers came and asked if any of them knew about any charms – and they replied, 'You did not help us to dismount, and you did not offer us a meal, so we will not help you until you give us a present.' So they made them a present of some sheep. Then the man was brought to them, and they recited the opening ayat of the Qur'an over him. And they recited ayat over him, and spat on the bite, until he was cured – and then the companions went off with the sheep, and they asked the Prophet about the affair. And he said, 'Who said that this was a charm? Eat up, and give me some!'" This hadith has been transmitted by al-Bukhari and Muslim.

Another version goes: "The villagers said, 'Do you have any medicine?' And they replied, 'Yes, but we will not give you any unless you pay us for it.'" This is the version of Abu Daw'ud.

Another version, also transmitted by Abu Daw'ud, goes: "They recited ayat of the Qur'an over him for three days, morning and evening. When they were finished, the sick man collected his spittle in his mouth and spat it out – and was freed, as if from a hobble."

Another version runs: "They brought along a man who was delirious or mad, tied up and bound."

Another version says: "They gave them one hundred ewes in return for the treatment."

The Umm al-Qur'an is the most useful surah of all to recite, because it contains glorification of Allah, together with worship of Him alone, and calling on Him for help. It is said that the exact point at which the cure is actually effected when reciting the ayat is at the words, **'Only You do we worship, and only You do we ask for help.'** (Qur'an: 1.4).

The Prophet, may Allah bless him and grant him peace, said, "Combining the recitation of ayat with charms is shirk." The reason for this statement is that in this case, shirk is being associated with the recitation of ayat. And so indeed it is. But when the recitation of ayat is free from shirk, then it is halal for Muslims to do so. There is nothing to prevent the recitation of ayat over a sick man, provided that there is no shirk involved.

Another version of what the Prophet said, may Allah bless him and grant him peace, goes: "A man came to the Prophet and said, 'O Messenger of Allah, you have forbidden the recitation of ayat over the sick, and yet I can cure scorpion stings by means of such recitation.' And the Prophet replied, 'Whoever among you is able to help his brother, should do so.'"

It is probable that this prohibition of something that was known to work was because some people believed that the cure came from the very nature of the words themselves. At a later stage, this prohibition was lifted. When Islam and the search for truth became established in their hearts, then he gave them permission to use such recitation, provided that they understood that it was Allah who effected the cure – or not. What is meant by a 'charm' is hanging beads around the neck – which some people think will ward off evil. This is sheer ignorance!

However, you should realise that there are some words which do indeed have an intrinsic quality which does have an effect, by the permission of Allah the Almighty. The testimony of many wise people bears witness to the truth of this. For what else can you think about the very words of Allah Himself, and the hadith which has been related from 'Ali, may Allah be pleased with him: "The Qur'an is the best of all medicines."? Ibn Maja has transmitted this hadith.

In their accepting a flock of sheep, there is proof that it is permissible to accept a fee for administering medicine, and to effect a cure by reciting ayat. Its permissibility is further confirmed by the Prophet's saying, may Allah bless him and grant him peace, "Eat up, and give me some!"

Furthermore, it is said that the flock was divided up in accordance with the wishes of the reciter who had been the means by which the cure was effected. Another commentator informs us that the reciter's name was Abu Sa'id al-Khudri. At least this is what the hadith says. This story has been included by at-Tirmidhi in his *Kitab al-Jama'*, in the section dealing with the fees of doctors. Abu Daw'ud also refers to it briefly in the section of his book that deals with the fees of physicians.

As regards spitting and blowing, the explanation of these will, I hope, come later, insh'Allah. (See page 158).

Examining the Sick

It has been related by Mujahid that Sa'd said, "Once I was sick, and the Prophet, may Allah bless him and grant him peace, came to visit me. He placed his hand between my nipples, until I felt its coolness penetrate the organs lying within my chest wall. He said, 'Truly, you are muf'ud.' So he sent for al-Harith ibn Kalda, from Thaqif, who is indeed an excellent physician." Note that a man is said to be 'muf'ud' when he has a disease of the organs that lie within the thorax.

Again, the Prophet, may Allah bless him and grant him peace, said, "When you have finished visiting someone who is sick, put your hand on his forehead and ask how he is feeling." This hadith has been transmitted by at-Tirmidhi.

It was the practice of the Prophet, may Allah bless him and grant him peace, whenever he entered the home of someone who was ill, to lay his hand on him. This hadith has been transmitted by al-Bukhari.

The Relationship between Examination and Treatment

Abu Sa'id said that the Prophet, may Allah bless him and grant him peace, said, "Treat the examiner who is a sincere believer with respect, for he sees by the light of Allah." And from the same source comes this hadith: "If you see a jaundiced-looking man who is not ill and who is not a worshipper, then know by this that in his heart he is not a true Muslim."

It has been related by Anas that the Prophet, may Allah bless him and grant him peace, said, "Truly Allah has slaves who are known to men simply by their looking at them." Abu Nu'aim has also transmitted this.

Physiognomy is the science of deducing what is inside by looking at what is visible outside. It is said to be a mental power that concentrates on the heart and rejects whatever is opposed to it. Its power over the heart is like a lion's power over its prey – and by means of this, the deduction is made.

When physiognomy is practised by an individual, his accuracy depends on the degree of his intelligence, his trust, and his understanding of the principles of this science. Allah the Almighty says:

**Surely in this there are signs
for those who can interpret them.**

(Qur'an: 15.75)

This also applies to physiognomists, and means: "I have examined him outwardly and found that he is well within," or, put more simply, "I have inspected him."

This science is particularly useful, when the cause of the illness is not clear. In this case, the physician will consider the temperament of the body, and make his diagnosis after examining its colour, its temperature, its feel, and its eyes.

Treatment by Members of the Opposite Sex Who are not Close Relations

Umm 'Atiyya said, "We travelled with the Prophet, may Allah bless him and grant him peace, on seven raids. I travelled at the rear with the baggage. I prepared their food, and I treated the sick and the wounded." This hadith has been transmitted by Muslim.

Anas said, "The Prophet, may Allah bless him and grant him peace, once went on a raid, and he took Umm Saylam with him, and with her came some of the womenfolk of the Ansar. They used to take the drinking water around, and they used to treat the wounded." This hadith has been transmitted by Muslim.

Ahmad says that it is halal for a physician to examine a woman, even though they are not related, whenever it is necessary to do so, and including even the private parts. This was also the view of al-Maruzi in his *Book of Ahadith*, and of al-Athram, and of Isma'il. Similarly, it is halal for a woman to look at the private parts of a man in a case of necessity. This is what Harab states in his collection of ahadith.

Al-Maruzi said, "Abu Abdullah's head was full of nits, so he asked a woman and she deloused him.

So it is clearly halal for a man to treat a woman to whom he is not related, and to see her private parts in cases of illness. And similarly it is halal for a woman to treat a man, and to see his private parts in a case of illness, and if there is no man or woman from his family at hand. Al-Maruzi said this in his *Book of Ahadith*.

In the same way, a witness is permitted to look at the face of a woman, and also whoever intends to conduct the marriage ceremony.

Again, if a man dies among women, or a woman dies among men, the women are permitted to wash the dead body of the man, and the men that of the woman. Thus there are two traditions, and in fact one complements the other.

Compelling the Sick to Eat and Drink

Ibn 'Amar said that the Prophet, may Allah bless him and grant him peace, said, "Do not force your sick to eat or to drink, for Allah gives them food, and Allah gives them drink." This has been transmitted by at-Tirmidhi, and Ibn Maja said that it is a sound hadith.

If a sick man has no desire to eat, because his constitution is battling against disease, or because he has lost his appetite, or because his faculties are weak, or for any other reason, then it is most improper to give him food at such a time – for if the sick man is forced to take food at this point, then the functions of his constitution will be weakened by it, and his energy will be diverted to digesting the food, instead of resisting and driving out the illness. So the food will actually do him harm, especially if it is at the critical point, because then it will only increase his pain.

At the critical point, nothing should be given except whatever conserves the faculties, such as small amounts of syrups with a well balanced temperament to drink, like syrups of roses and apples, or chicken broth – and whatever else will stimulate the faculties because it has a pleasing aroma – or a little bread.

A patient who is unconscious may have to be force fed.

Sometimes a sick man has no desire for food because his body is over-congested. If this is the case, and you feed him, then you will only make his condition worse.

Both Hippocrates and Ibn Sina said, "Food is a friend of the faculties as far as its being food is concerned, but it is also their enemy when it is perceived that it is also the friend of their enemy." By 'the enemy' of the faculties they mean the parts which are diseased.

The meaning of the words of the Prophet, may Allah bless him and grant him peace, which were quoted above – "… Allah gives them food, and Allah gives them drink …" – is that it is Allah Who sustains the sick as if they were being given food, and as if they were being given drink, by Him. And so there is no harm in their having nothing to eat or drink. And there is the other hadith of the Prophet, may Allah bless him and grant him peace: "I am not like any one of you, for I dwell with Allah, and He gives me food and He gives me drink."

Giving the Sick Whatever they Want to Eat

It has been related by Ibn Abbas that the Prophet, may Allah bless him and grant him peace, visited a sick man and asked him what he would like. The man replied, "Wheat bread." According to another version of this hadith, the man said, "Plain cake." And the Prophet said, "Whoever has any wheat bread should send some to his brother." And he added, "If any one of you is sick, and he has an appetite for something, then he should eat it." This hadith has been transmitted by Ibn Maja.

If a sick man eats what he wants, then even if there is some harm in it, it will still be more beneficial and less harmful for him, than if he were to eat something which he does not want, even though there is some benefit in it. And if what he wants only has good in it, then there is nothing better than it. Whenever the appetite is normal, it is necessary for the physician to pay attention to what the appetite of the sick man desires.

Hippocrates said, "Preference should be given to whatever food or drink appears more pleasant – even if it is not so good – over whatever is most nutritious.

Withholding Whatever will Make the Illness Grow Worse

Ja'far ibn Muhammad, who heard this story from his father, said, "Someone gave the Prophet, may Allah bless him and grant him peace, a bag of dates at a time when 'Ali, may Allah be pleased with him, had a fever. The Prophet gave him a date, and then another, and another, until he had let him eat seven. Then he said, 'That is enough for you.' He, may Allah bless him and grant him peace, did this because there is something in dates which is bad for people who have a fever, and which gives them headaches and makes them thirsty – but if they only have a few, then this harm does not come to them."

Vegetarian Meals for the Sick

We have already quoted the hadith concerning Umm al-Manzir, and her words, "... I prepared a meal of spinach and barley for them." (See page 128).

The following has been related by 'Ayesha, may Allah be pleased with her: "Whenever any of the companions of the Prophet were not well, may the blessings and peace of Allah be on him and on his family and his companions, he would order a soup to be made for them, and he would make them drink the soup. He used to say that it would comfort the innermost parts of the afflicted, and ease the innermost parts of the sick, wiping away affliction and sickness just as dust is wiped away from the face." This hadith has been transmitted by at-Tirmidhi.

In this account, 'were not well' means 'had a fever', and 'a soup' means a dish of flour, water and fat, all boiled together. A meal of this comforts the inner parts of the one who is afflicted – that is to say, it fortifies and strengthens him, wiping away and dissolving all the pain from his innermost parts.

Again, it has been related by 'Ayesha, may Allah be pleased with her, "If the Prophet, may Allah bless him and grant him peace, was ever told that someone was off his food, he used to say, 'Make him some talabina soup, and give it to him to eat.'" And she also said, "The Prophet, may Allah bless him and grant him peace, said, 'Talabina soup fills up the inner parts of a sick man to the brim and drives away sorrow.'" This has been transmitted by al-Bukhari.

Please note that talabina soup is a soup made from flour or bran, and is often sweetened with honey. It is called 'talabina' from the word 'labn', which means 'milk', because since it is white, it looks like milk. It is a very filling soup, and affords a great deal of relief. Some say that it is a mild laxative, and others say that it constipates. Now grief and sorrow do indeed cool down the temperament, and weaken inner energy – and this soup fortifies inner energy and heats it up. The words 'innermost parts' indicate here the cardia of the stomach.

'Ayesha herself, may Allah be pleased with her, has related that she used to order talabina soup, saying that it was awful, but efficacious. A hadith states that she herself ordered talabina soup for patients. Al-Bukhari has transmitted this. She used the word 'awful' because patients used to dislike it and refuse to take it.

The author of this book says that if you want to measure the efficacy of soup, then you must measure the efficacy of barley water, especially when it is combined with bran. Soup brightens people up as it permeates rapidly throughout the body, and it provides tasty nourishment, especially when taken hot, in which case its benefits are even greater, its tonic action is more rapid, and its brightening up effect is enhanced.

Minor Services for the Sick

Bandaging the Head

It has been related by Ibn 'Abbas that during his last illness, the Prophet, may Allah bless him and grant him peace, came out with his head bound up with a piece of cloth. He sat like this on the mimbar and praised Allah. The hadith praises him at great length for this, and extols his name. The complete hadith has been transmitted by al-Bukhari.

Muhammad, may Allah bless him and grant him peace, used to bandage his head very tightly. By doing this, the head is fortified, and pain is alleviated.

Shaving the Head

Al-Bukhari has written some sections on this subject, quoting Ka'ab ibn 'Ajra, who said, "During the time of the Prophet, may Allah bless him and grant him peace, I was standing below the mimbar, when a louse crawled out from my head. The Prophet said, 'Could this be from you?' And I replied, 'Yes.' So he said to me, 'Then shave your scalp.' This hadith has been transmitted by al-Bukhari.

Shaving the head opens the pores, soothes headaches, and fortifies the whole head. Ibn 'Abbas was of the opinion that shaving the nape of the neck strengthens the neck.

Using Snuff when Sick

Ibn 'Abbas said that the Prophet, may Allah bless him and grant him peace, used to use snuff. This is generally agreed upon.

The words 'use snuff' mean inserting a remedy into the nostril. Snuff is often used to make a man go to sleep, and to calm him down. It is because of this that physicians sometimes order the nose and limbs of a sick man to be anointed with violet oil.

Washing the Sick

It has been confirmed by the *Sahih* of al-Bukhari that the Prophet, may Allah bless him and grant him peace, ordered seven containers of water to be poured over him during his illness, because this livens up a sick man, makes it easier for him to sleep, and strengthens his faculties.

Visits by the Sick

It has been related by Abu Huraira that the Prophet, may Allah bless him and grant him peace, said, "Someone who is ill should not go and visit the healthy." It has also been related by Ibn 'Abbas that the Prophet said, "Do not gaze at a leper for any length of time." This has been transmitted by Ibn Maja. And al-Bukhari added, "Flee from someone who has leprosy as you would flee from a lion."

It has been related by Jabir that the Prophet, may Allah bless him and grant him peace, took hold of the hand of a leper and put it in the same dish as his own, saying, "Eat in the Name of Allah." This has been transmitted by at-Tirmidhi and Ibn Maja. A similar hadith has been related by Ibn 'Umar, who said that there was a leper amongst the delegation from Thaqif. The Prophet said to him, "You may return now, for we have accepted your allegiance." This has been transmitted by Muslim and an-Nasa'i.

As regards the words of the Prophet, may Allah bless him and grant him peace, "Someone who is ill should not go and visit the healthy," this does not refer to a man himself who is sick, but rather means a man whose cattle are sick. Such a person should not visit a man whose cattle are healthy, for if, by the will of Allah, the healthy cattle should perhaps fall ill, their owner might think that this co-incidence had resulted from that visit.

The Prophet, may Allah bless him and grant him peace, said, "There is no such thing as a contagious illness, nor is there any such thing as an evil omen." Such conceptions should be avoided.

Leprosy

Leprosy is the result of black bile spreading throughout the body. It corrupts the temperament of the organs, and their shape. It often eats them up and causes them to drop off. The disease of leprosy is also called 'leontiasis', either because lions frequently suffer from it, or because the face of someone who suffers from leprosy comes to resemble that of a lion.

Physicians maintain that leprosy is both contagious and heredi-tary.

The Prophet, may Allah bless him and grant him peace, for-bade gazing at a leper for any length of time. He once sent for a leper, and then told him to return. He also once shared a meal with a leper. In other words, he avoided one in order to demonstrate caution, and ate with the other in order to show that it is permissi-ble.

Ibn Qatayba said, "Whoever comes near a leper will himself become sick – from the smell, not from the disease." 'Ayesha, may Allah be pleased with her, said, "This statement is refuted by the words of the Prophet, may Allah bless him and grant him peace, that there is no such thing as a contagious disease – and by his eating with a leper." And as for his words, "Flee from someone who has leprosy ...", this is an order making such action permissi-ble. Whoever cannot bear to see a leper's suffering should shun him. And it is indeed the smell that makes him infectious. And there is no power except from Allah.

Using Haram Remedies

I have already discussed the ahadith related by Tariq ibn Suwayd and others concerning the fact that it is haram to treat people with wine and substances like it. (See pages 53 to 54).

Please note that the word 'khamr' and 'khamrah' (meaning 'wine' – and by analogy anything that is alcoholic or intoxicating) appears in both the masculine and the feminine form, and one may write 'khamr' or 'khamrah'.

The best of the truthful ones, may Allah bless him and grant him peace, once stated that wine is not a medicine, but rather a disease – because it contains harmful elements that cause damage and rob a man of his senses. And if a man loses his common sense, then he loses his iman. And if he loses his iman, then that man is heading for the Fire. May Allah the Almighty preserve us from that!

Hippocrates said, "The harm that wine does to the head is serious, because it harms the intellect. The author of the *Royal Book* says that its particular property is that it damages the brain and the nerves. Others have said that it causes forgetfulness and sudden death, as well as making what is bad appear good. It may also cause shaking palsies, facial palsies, muscular palsies, apoplexy, and other similar conditions.

'Ayesha, may Allah be pleased with her, said that the Prophet, may Allah bless him and grant him peace, said, "Anything that intoxicates is haram, and whatever intoxicates the power of discrimination, even if it is a small amount, is haram." This hadith has been transmitted by at-Tirmidhi and Abu Daw'ud.

It is well known that wine used to be considered a remedy for certain diseases. It may well be that Allah the Almighty removed any benefits that it may have had when He made wine haram – and this he made known to the Prophet, may Allah bless him and grant him peace, who then said, "Wine is a disease, and not a medicine."

Shaykh Muhiyu'd-Din at-Tawawi said that the Prophet, may Allah bless him and grant him peace, said, "Whoever breaks his fast with seven 'Ajwat dates will not be harmed by any poison or sorcery during that day." And he added, "This is an excellent piece of knowledge, and the shari'ah confirms it." And I myself say that Shaykh Muhiyu'd-Din spoke the truth, may Allah have mercy on him.

These facts were not known by any physician, or by anyone, or even by any of the earlier Prophets, peace be on them. No one, except the Prophet Muhammad, may Allah bless him and grant him peace, drew attention to these facts. However, some of the physicians who came later have claimed that 'Ajwat dates are a remedy for cold poisons, and that this was why Allah removed any benefit from wine – a fact which He revealed only to the Prophet when He made wine haram.

In the version transmitted by Abu Talib, the words of Abu Thawar were put to Ahmad: "Do you treat your patients with wine?" And he replied, "That is an absolutely awful question!"

In the same context, it has been reported by al-Maruzi that when the words of Abu Thawar were put to Ahmad, he replied, "Even if the physicians are united in giving wine to those who are ill, I still utterly condemn it!"

Nor is it halal to treat people with a syrup that contains snake flesh in wine. According to al-Maruzi's book, he said, "Even if it only contains snake flesh, I still do not think that it should be taken." Similarly, he said, "Even if it is mixed with asses' milk, it should not be drunk, even in dire necessity." And the same is true if it is mixed with asses' urine. Support for this is to be found in a hadith which was related by Abu Huraira, who said that the Prophet, may Allah bless him and grant him peace, said, "Whoever is treated with a remedy that Allah has made halal will be cured, but whoever is treated with a remedy that Allah has made haram will certainly not be allowed by Allah to be cured." And the Prophet made asses' flesh, and their milk, haram on the Day of Khaybar.

It is permissible to drink camels' urine in cases of necessity. This has been related in the ahadith transmitted by Saleh, Ibn Hanbal, 'Abdullah, al-Athram, and Ibrahim ibn al-Harath. As for whether or not drinking it is permitted when there is no dire necessity, the generally accepted opinion is that it is permitted, by virtue of the hadith from 'Anas which has already been quoted above. (See pages 93 to 94).

Taking narcotic drugs is haram. One of these is the drug which is known as 'ad-dari', which is a seed resembling a barley-seed, and black in colour. Another example is henbane, which is called 'al-banj', and which causes intoxication.

We have already mentioned the fact that the Prophet, may Allah bless him and grant him peace, forbade frogs to be killed in order to be eaten. (See pages 53 and 75). This prohibition against killing them is because they are classed as a poison. It is true that this prohibition has not been very well publicised or brought to peoples' attention, but the reason for this prohibition is because there is much that is harmful in frogs. Whoever eats the flesh of some species of frog will have their teeth fall out – and this applies even to the teeth of domestic animals. If they so much as graze on the grass, (where frogs have been), their bodies swell and their colouring changes. Indeed, it has been said that whoever eats frogs will continue to discharge semen until he perishes!

The yellow species of frog is the most harmful.

Now, if physicians have refrained from using them as a remedy out of their sympathy for mankind, then how could the Prophet fail to do so, may Allah bless him and grant him peace, whom all the believers know is gentle and compassionate, (and which I swear to, by my father and mother!)?

Treating Fevers

Treating Fevers with Cold Water

Physicians say that drinking cold water when a fever is just beginning weakens and dissipates the energy of a sick person.

A well known hadith states that Ibn 'Umar said, "Fever is from the raging heat of the Fire, so cool it down with water." This hadith has been transmitted by al-Bukhari and by Muslim.

A similar hadith has been related by Ibn 'Abbas: "Fever is from the boiling heat of Hell, so put it out with the water of Zamzam." This hadith has been transmitted by al-Bukhari.

The following account has come from Asma' bint Abi Bakr: A severe kind of headache used to make a certain woman sometimes roll in the dust in pain. So she would call for water, and pour it over her forehead. Then she would say, "Truly the Prophet, may Allah bless him and grant him peace, said, "Cool it down with water, because it is from the breath of the Fire." This has been transmitted by al-Bukhari and by Muslim.

The words of the Prophet, may Allah bless him and grant him peace, "Cool it down with water ..." are particularly relevant to the people of the Hijaz, for if heat overcomes them, they drink cool water, or bathe in it, because it helps them deal with their hot climate. Cold water cools down a fever and overcomes its heat and burning fire. And the words of the Prophet, "... it is from the breath of the Fire," indicate the violence of the heat and its intensity. And may Allah the Almighty in His mercy protect us from this. And the words of the Prophet, "... put it out with the water of Zamzam," demonstrate that this water is particularly excellent. For different waters have different effects on different diseases, depending also on the baraka that they have. Thus the Prophet, may Allah bless him and grant him peace, said, "When the water of Zamzam is drunk, the emaciated and the feverish are cured."

According to Anas, the Prophet, may Allah bless him and grant him peace, also said, "If any one of you has a fever, then pour cold water over him on three successive nights at dawn." This hadith has been transmitted by al-Juzi.

It has been related by Abu Huraira that the Prophet, may Allah bless him and grant him peace, said, "Fever is a draught from the draught of the Fire, so keep it away from you by using cold water." This has been transmitted by Ibn Maja.

This hadith comes from Sumra: "Putting out a fever is like damping down a fire, so cool it down with water."

It was the practice of the Prophet, may Allah bless him and grant him peace, when he was feverish, to ask for containers of water, and to pour the water over his head and wash himself. This hadith has been transmitted by al-Hassan, quoting Sumra.

It has been related by 'Ayesha, may Allah be pleased with her, that the Prophet, may Allah bless him and grant him peace, said, "Be generous to me in my illness, and pour seven water-skins of water over me."

From Rafa' ibn Hadij comes this hadith: "If an attack of fever seizes any one of you, truly fever is part of the Fire, so put it out with cold water." This hadith has been transmitted by at-Tirmidhi.

Galen said, "If a young man who is fat bathes in water during the hot season, it will not be good for him."

I maintain that it is the general opinion of physicians that water is the best of drinks, for it drives out a hot fever, thanks to its subtlety, the speed with which it penetrates, and the lightness of its effect on the constitution.

When treating some conditions, it is necessary to make the water even cooler, in which case ice is added to it; or else its strength and power of penetration have to be increased, in which case vinegar is added to it; or else its wetness and capacity to reach distant organs have to be improved, in which case the vinegar is balanced with sugar, and the sugar by the vinegar. The result is known as an oxymel. And this is a most useful remedy for treating those who are afflicted with feverishness in their diseased organs, because of its piercing and gently laxative properties.

Varieties of Fevers

There are several varieties of fever. One of them is a diurnal fever which will often finish its course in a single day, but may continue for three days. This type is connected with the humours, and is known as a 'putrid fever'. When the fever is connected with the main organs, it is called a 'hectic fever'. This type of fever often acts as a purifying agent for thick humours, and can cure paralysis and dissolve colic and so forth.

It has been related from Abu Huraira that he said, "I was once having a conversation with the Prophet, may Allah bless him and grant him peace, and I said that fever was a curse for people – but he replied, 'It is not a curse, for it purifies wrong action just as fire purifies the impurities in iron.'" This hadith has been transmitted by Ibn Maja.

And from Jabir comes this: "The Prophet, may Allah bless him and grant him peace, came into see Umm Sa'ib, or Umm Musayyab, and said, 'Why are you shivering?' And she replied, 'I have a fever – and there is no blessing from Allah in it!' And he said, 'Do not curse it, for truly fever removes the wrong actions of the Tribe of Adam just as bellows help to remove the impurities from iron.'" Muslim has transmitted this hadith.

There is a hadith that says that the Prophet, may Allah bless him and grant him peace, said, "Having a fever for a day is like fasting for a year."

It has been related by al-Hassan that the Prophet, may Allah bless him and grant him peace, said, "Truly, all a worshipper's wrong actions will be effaced if he suffers from fever for a night."

So having a fever is beneficial, both for one's body and for one's faith, and this is why the Prophet, may Allah bless him and grant him peace, has forbidden people to curse fever.

Signs of Various Fevers

The signs of a fever which is due to Blood are redness in the face and eyes. It is treated with blood letting, scarification, and drinking sour infusions.

The signs of a fever which is due to Bile are yellowness in the face, insomnia, vomiting bile, and a bitter taste in the mouth. It is treated by taking prune syrup and sour meat dishes. In cases where there is much thirst, green melons, milk, and beans or purslane seeds should be taken. The constitution should be made to relax with infusions that will induce a flow. If insomnia is predominant, then oil of violets should be inserted in the patient's nostrils. If the faculties grow weak, feed him with chicken soup. If the disease becomes prolonged, then induce a flow with rhubarb linctus. When the fever diminishes, make the patient have a hot bath and eat lambs' meat.

The signs of a fever which is due to Phlegm are lack of thirst, a grey complexion, and shivering. The shivering is treated by using emetics and making the patient drink hot water with any kind of oxymel. At the same time, the constitution should be relaxed with laxative enemas, and at a later stage with cassia linctus. The patient should be fed with soured chicken meat and saff flower.

The signs of a fever which is due to Spleen are a livid complexion or face, and the urine, and excessive insomnia. At the onset of the fever, the urine looks like barley water. The best foods when treating this kind of patient are those which produce wetness and induce sleep. The best food, in terms of both quality and quantity, is a drink made with one ounce of one of the above mixed with half an ounce of sugar. The constitution should also be made to flow by using decoctions. The patient should be fed on kids' flesh, fresh fish and pulses.

All of these fevers are accompanied by vertigo.

The distinguishing feature of a bilious fever is the frequency with which it occurs, for there is a fever one day, and then none on the next – that is, it is a tertian fever.

A splenic fever also has a certain frequency, where there is a fever one day, and then none for the next two days – that is, it is a quartan fever.

With a phlegmy fever, however, the fever occurs every day – that is, it is a quotidian fever.

At their onset, all types of fever should be treated with emetics. The treatment after that is as described above.

However, if the fever is connected with the main organs, and is accompanied by a cough, persistent feverishness, a dislike for taking any food, and with sweating and general weakness, then barley water which is thick with pearls of barley must be given. If the patient is overcome with thirst, then he must take camphor pills if he is strong enough to do so – otherwise they should not be given to him. He should have plenty of hot baths and stay in a room which does not have fresh air coming into it. He should not abandon this, nor stop eating thin chicken soup, kids' flesh, gravy made from fowls, with white barley bread soaked in it, or cheese and poppy heads. And if, even after all this, his condition deteriorates, then expect death. And Allah knows everything.

Treating Minor Ailments

Headaches

A headache may be due to Blood, or to Phlegm, or to Spleen.

We have already discussed its treatment in the section on remedies for fevers. In addition, however, in cases of a cold headache, the patient should sniff musk, amber and coriander. He should be given honey to eat. He should take hot ebullients and hot enemas. He should avoid drinking cold water and cold draughts. If he needs to take an emetic, he should have a hickory pill.

The regime described above should be followed when treating all cold diseases of the brain, such as epilepsy, apoplexy, palsy, facial paralysis, tremors, one-sided headaches, flaccid paralysis, coma, and catarrhal discharges from the brain, whether anterior or posterior.

To make a hickory pill, take one drachm of hickory, one drachm of white turpeth, one sixth of a drachm of scammony, and two parts of tragacanth. Prepare one pill from all of this, to be taken last thing at night.

We have already quoted the hadith which has been related by Abu Huraira that whenever the Prophet, may Allah bless him and grant him peace, had a sudden headache, he would dye his head with henna. Ibn Maja refers to this hadith also. And we have already discussed the benefits that henna has. (See pages 55 to 57).

Anyone who wants to have good health must avoid extreme heat and cold, violent winds, smoke and dust, crying too much, straining the eyes when writing, and reading small writing for too long. This last activity should indeed be done, but not too often, for if it is done a little, it sharpens the eyesight. A person should also avoid looking at shining objects, at the orb of the sun, and at whatever is pure black or pure white.

The best colour for the eyes to gaze at is green. It has been related by Anas that of all the colours, the most pleasing to the Prophet, may Allah bless him and grant him peace, was green. And Allah the Almighty Himself has said:

... and they shall wear green robes of fine silk and brocade ...

(Qur'an: 18.31)

Green is said to be the colour of the clothes of the people of Syria in the Garden. It has been related by Ibn 'Abbas that the Prophet, may Allah bless him and grant him peace, admired anything that was green because it improved the eyesight. And, according to al-Bukhari, the same is true of looking at running water. It helps the eyes by strengthening them. It also protects the health of the eyes, just like scented antimony does – a subject which we have already discussed. (See pages 35 to 36).

Nose-bleeds

Bleeding from the nose should not be stopped, unless it becomes copious and weakening, in which case, the patient should take apple syrup and camphor, and have his strength restored by eating chicken soup.

Teeth

Teeth can be protected by avoiding chewing the various kinds of gums, by not cracking hard objects with them, by not eating very cold foods, and by avoiding extreme cold, especially just after eating hot food. Similarly, hot food should be avoided just after drinking cold water. Excessive use of a tooth-stick ruins the teeth and hurts the mouth, as do all foods that need to be ground up. Eating the green leaves of leeks is bad for them, because of a particular property that they have.

Coughs

The way to treat a cough is to take barley water, sweet ebullients, pomegranates prepared with almond oil, milky dishes, and soft boiled eggs. Eating snow, meat, and anything that is acidic or salty, should be avoided.

Liver Pains and Colic

Pain in the liver and colic is often caused by eating too much wind-producing food, such as peas, lentils, dry beans, and the entry of food on food. These can be treated by vomiting, avoiding the above foods, eating a confection of roses with warm water, laxative and sour enemas if required, purgative quince syrup, rubbing the liver area of the belly with rose oil and mastic, or applying a hot bran poultice, and having a hot bath.

Gripes and Tenesmus

The way to treat the gripes and tenesmus is to boil mallow juice with apple syrup. Mix this while still hot with whole flea wort seeds, and stir the mixture into hot water in which poppy heads have been boiled. If the spasm is extreme, a tenesmus suppository should be inserted. The patient should drink a soup made from both old and unripe grapes. If the diarrhoea is excessive, take syrup of pomegranates combined with powdered pomegranate seeds.

Pleurisy

As regards treating pleurisy, we have already described the treatment for pseudo pleurisy. (See page 87). Real pleurisy should be treated with ebullients and a paste made from barley flour, white mallow, and violet blossom. The patient should take barley water with almond oil, and if the bowels are constipated, he should have cassia pods with refined sugar.

Dropsy

As regards treating dropsy, we have already discussed it. (See pages 93 to 95).

It has been related by Abu Huraira that the Prophet, may Allah bless him and grant him peace, told a physician to make an incision in the abdomen of a man who had a chronic disease of the stomach. He said, "O Messenger of Allah, can the art of medicine be of any help in this case?" And the Prophet replied, "If this kind of treatment has ever proved successful, then let this method of treatment also be used here, just as in the case of a man who in the opinion of the physicians ought to be treated by means of paracentesis because he has dropsy."

Among the different types of dropsy, there is one known as 'ascites'. This is the worst kind, although others say that the type known as 'anasarca' is worse.

Enuresis

As regards enuresis, this occurs mainly among children and the elderly. It is caused by the cold, and it is therefore advisable to give them more clothes to wear. People with this problem should break their fast with gum-incense, mastic and honey, and they should avoid soups, cold meals, water melons, sugar cane, and similar foods.

Piles

The way to treat piles is to take spinach syrup with hot water, and eat preparations made from marsh mallow, common mallow, and spinach. The patient should also eat foods that relax the constitution as much as possible, and he should avoid dry bread and anything else that is an absorbent.

Rheumatism

The way to treat rheumatism is by vomiting, and avoiding fleshy food, especially fish, milk, and fresh fruit. The patient should eat honey and other hot foods, if his rheumatism is due to the cold, and he should take purgative pills.

Sciatica

The way to treat sciatica has already been described under the letter 'Alif', including the recommendation of the Prophet, may Allah bless him and grant him peace, with regard to this. (See page 38).

There is a hadith that says that a certain Jew suffered from sciatica. So he gave up camels' milk and camels' meat and made them haram for himself. And he was cured. And then he made them haram for his children as well. And I too maintain that milk and meat – especially camels' and cows' meat – are very bad for pain in the joints and in the sciatic nerve. Ibn Sina states that meat and wine are haram for those who suffer from rheumatism.

It should be known that the word 'sciatica' refers to a pain that starts in the hip joint, passes down from the buttocks to the thigh, and even continues down to the heel. The longer it lasts, the greater is the pain, and it makes the leg waste away.

Cauterisation

Should people use cautery? There are two answers to this question, and both have been verified. One hadith, which has been related by Jabir, states that the Prophet, may Allah bless him and grant him peace, said, "If you have any choice in your treatment, as to whether you should choose scarification or cauterisation with fire, then personally I do not like cauterisation." This hadith has been transmitted by al-Bukhari and by Muslim.

A hadith which has been related by Ibn 'Abbas states that the Prophet, may Allah bless him and grant him peace, said, "If the cure ultimately depends on either scarification, or drinking honey, or cauterisation with fire, then I absolutely forbid cauterisation." This hadith has been transmitted by al-Bukhari.

In his *Ahadith,* and in his books on paracentesis and cauterisation, al-Bukhari says, "Abu 'Abdullah al-Marzi said, as we have already related, that as regards other congestive diseases – whether they are due to Blood, or Bile, or Phlegm, or Spleen – the way to cure those due to Blood is by blood letting, and the way to cure other congestive diseases is by using remedies that provoke a flow which is appropriate for the particular humour in question.

The Prophet, may Allah bless him and grant him peace, preferred scarification over cauterisation for the purposes of blood letting, and put phlebotomy after scarification. He also preferred the use of honey syrup over that of purgatives.

It is only when all other remedies have failed, that the physician should try cautery. It should only be used when the strongest medicines have been defeated by the constitution, and no other remedy has proved successful. By means of the following hadith, the Prophet, may Allah bless him and grant him peace, showed us what to do by prescribing basic treatment for simple diseases, when he said, "Truly the intensity of a fever is from the raging heat of the Fire, so cool it down with water." His words, and some lines of poetry, will be discussed later, insh'Allah.

The following hadith has been related by Jabir: "Sa'd ibn Mu'adh suffered from conjunctivitis, which was due to scabies, so the Prophet, may Allah bless him and grant him peace, let some blood from his arm by using a mishqas arrow. The swelling returned, so he let some more blood a second time." This hadith has been transmitted by Muslim.

'Amran ibn al-Hasbayni has related the hadith which states that the Prophet, may Allah bless him and grant him peace, prohibited cauterisation, saying, "We were afflicted with a disease and branded ourselves, but we were not successful, and the branding was of no benefit to us." This hadith has been transmitted by Abu Daw'ud, by an-Nasa'i and by Ibn Maja.

It has been related by Ibn 'Abbas that the Prophet, may Allah bless him and grant him peace, said, "There will be 70,000 thousand of my followers – not counting those who refuse to consult soothsayers – who will enter the Garden because they do not believe in bad omens, nor use cautery, but rely on their Lord." Al-Bukhari and Muslim have transmitted this hadith.

Please note, with regard to the above ahadith, that the word 'mihjam' used by the Prophet, may Allah bless him and grant him peace – with 'i' as its first vowel – means 'scarification by a professional blood-letter'. This word also means 'the bowl in which the blood that exudes after scarification is collected'. The word 'ladha't', with a dhal-i-mu'ajama and an 'ayn-i-muhmala – that is, with a dotted 'Dhal' and an undotted ''Ayn' – means 'light cautery'.

Furthermore, the 'akhal' vein is a vein in the middle of the forearm, which is used for blood letting.

The word 'mishqas' – with 'i' as its first vowel – means 'a long thin arrow-head'. A broad arrow-head is known as 'al-ma'ila'.

The word 'hasama' means 'to let blood by means of scarification'.

Finally, the words 'those who refuse to consult soothsayers' mean that one should not ask another to recite incantations as a charm. And the words 'they do not believe in bad omens' refers to those people who pay no attention to omens which would contradict their trust in Allah – and how blessed that trust is!

As regards the ahadith to which we have just referred, some appear to permit the use of cautery, and others seem to forbid it. The correct view is mid-way between the two. The prohibition relates to the mental state of those who rely on cautery , when they think that it is the cauterisation itself which cures the affliction, believing that if cautery had not been used, then the patient would have perished. It was cauterisation practised with this kind of reliance that resulted in its being prohibited. On the other hand, however, cautery is permitted when it is perceived as being the appropriate means to effect a cure, but not the essential cause of the cure. For it is Allah alone Who cures and grants good health – not cauterisation nor medicines.

In this context, many people express views which demonstrate their doubt concerning the truth of this. For instance, they will say, "If so-and-so had taken this medicine, he wouldn't be dead now." Or again, "If so-and-so had remained in his own country, he wouldn't have been killed."

It is safe to assume that the use of cautery is forbidden if it was going to be used merely as a means of preventing disease, and before it was really needed – for this is reprehensible. However, in a case of necessity, then it becomes permitted.

It is equally safe to assume that the prohibition against utilising cautery applies for as long as complete trust in Allah is lacking. It can also be assumed that it may be used, and is fully permitted, whenever there is no other alternative – for example, where a wound has pierced an artery, and the bleeding will not normally stop unless it is cauterised with fire. This is because the pumping in the artery prevents the blood from clotting. When, however, cautery is applied, the cauterisation forms a scab at the mouth of the wound, so that the blood which is flowing from the puncture in the artery can cling to it at the mouth of the wound and clot, thereby stopping the bleeding. Forming a clot in this manner is achieved by the use of common sense and by the permission of Allah – and surely no one can be blamed for resorting to cautery in circumstances such as these.

Al-Khattabi said, "Truly the Prophet, may Allah bless him and grant him peace, cauterised Sa'd in order to stop a haemorrhage which otherwise would have been fatal."

And after amputating a hand or a foot, the wound is cauterised with the same intention. Cauterisation in such cases is a matter of obligation.

There is a helpful hadith that states that Ibn 'Umar used to use cautery for treating facial palsy. It has been related by Abu Zubayr, as follows: "I saw Ibn 'Umar one day, and he was branding the forehead of a man who had a slight facial palsy." Now, facial palsy is caused by diseased matter which is thick. It is classified as being one of the chronic diseases, and the diseased matter which pro-

duces it cannot be dissolved by any medicine. Thus, in these circumstances, branding is the best way of treating it.

Sprains, Fractures and Bites

Sprains

The way to treat a sprain is by evacuating the blood, leaving the
muscle tissue intact, and applying ice.

It has been related by Jabir: "I once cupped the Prophet on his
hips, may Allah bless him and grant him peace, because of a sprain
from which he was suffering." Abu Daw'ud has also transmitted
this hadith.

A sprain is defined as being a weakness where there is no frac-
ture or dislocation of the bones. Treating a sprain also involves
strengthening the surrounding area by rubbing on an ointment
made from sesame leaves and myrtle which have been mixed together in a bowl.

Fractures

Al-Jabr said, "'Ali, may Allah be pleased with him, broke one of
the bones in his forearm, so I set it. I asked the Prophet, may Allah
bless him and grant him peace, about it, and he said, 'Put ointment
on it, and carry on applying the ointment while the arm is in the
splint until it has healed.'"

Bites from Rabid Dogs

Rabies is a form of madness which occurs in dogs when their temperament becomes a splenic temperament.

The signs of rabies are: the eyes are red, the tongue hangs out of
the mouth with a great deal of slobbering, the animal hangs its
head down near to the ground, its ears are floppy, its tail droops
between its legs, and its coat is dishevelled. The dog runs here and
there continuously, staggering like a drunkard. It will attack anyone it sees. It hardly barks at all, but if it does, the sound is hoarse.
Other dogs avoid it and will not share their food with it. It flees
from water as soon as it catches sight of it.

If a rabid dog bites someone, the symptoms which occur in the person are almost exactly the same as those displayed by the rabid dog. The disease which then develops in that person is one of the most terrible diseases there are. The person is terrified by water whenever he sees it. He flees in fear from anyone whom he sees or who approaches him. If he looks at himself in a mirror, he sees the face of a dog.

The Prophet, may Allah bless him and grant him peace, said "If a rabid dog has put its nose into one of your pots, then wash the pot seven times, including once with earth." Another version of this hadith goes, "… seven times, the first being with earth." This is a very sound hadith, because the rabies poison is transmitted through the saliva – so when a dog thrusts its nose into a container, the poison finds its way into the container along with the saliva, just as it found its way into the body when it was bitten. The diseased matter in the saliva would have the same effect on anyone who ate from that container as it would on anyone who had been bitten. And that is why the Prophet told people to wash any container into which a rabid dog has dribbled, in order to prevent any chance of harm. Such was the concern that the Prophet had for his community, may the blessings and peace of Allah be on him and on his family and companions and followers.

Anyone who has been bitten by a rabid dog begins to be afraid of water after an interval of one to two weeks, up to six months. If there is some doubt as to whether or not the dog which inflicted the bite is rabid, take a piece of bread and sprinkle some of the blood that runs from the bite onto it, and then give it to another dog to eat. If it eats the bread, then the dog which bit the person is not rabid, but if it refuses to eat the bread, then the first dog is rabid.

As regards treatment, the site of the bite must first be excised, and then cupping should be used. A very strong suction must be created, and care should be taken to ensure that the wound remains open, so that the diseased matter can exit. The patient should be given barley, and young kids' meat to eat, and should be made to rest.

Sometimes the person who has been bitten will pass tiny lumps of extraordinary looking flesh in his urine, which look a little like tiny dogs!

It is most necessary for the person who sucks the air out of the cups during the cupping to rub his mouth with rose oil just before he starts sucking.

Snake Bites

Whoever has been bitten by a snake must be deprived of sleep, because during sleep the poison penetrates deep into the body. Cups should be applied to the site of the bite and the air sucked out, exactly as just described above. Blood letting is beneficial if the poison has spread throughout the body, but it is of no use in the early stages.

Scorpion Stings

There are two conditions that result from a scorpion sting, one hot and the other cold.

In both cases, the treatment is to split open the scorpion, apply it to the site of the sting, and bind it there very tightly. Make the patient eat hazel nuts and orange pips. This has been proved through experience.

We have already mentioned that the Prophet, may Allah bless him and grant him peace, had salt and water applied to a scorpion sting, (see page 104). According to the hadith, the Prophet killed the scorpion and then asked for salt and water, which he then poured over the finger that had been stung.

A Du'a for Protection during the Night

Whoever recites the words of Allah in their entirety (i.e. the whole of the Qur'an) when night falls, will be protected by Allah from all harmful creatures because of that. Such a person can not be harmed by scorpions until after the day has safely dawned.

Similarly, whoever of the believers makes this du'a when the night comes – "In the Name of Allah, with Whose Name nothing in the earth or in the heavens can be harmed, and He is the Hearing, the Knowing," – can not be harmed before the following morning comes.

Avoiding Pests at Night

It once used to be the custom of physicians to keep cats, storks, peacocks and hedgehogs in their homes (to get rid of pests), and to light lamps and lanterns in their houses at night, so that flying insects would fly into them. All these measures were taken in order to prevent the harm that such pests can do.

The Prophet, may Allah bless him and grant him peace, was different to such people, for he said, "When you go to sleep, put out your lamps." And he also said, "Do not leave a fire alight in your house while you are asleep." He also said, "Fire is your enemy, so put it out when you are sleeping." And he also said, "The fawaisaqa often falls on the wick and sets fire to the people in the house." All these ahadith are sound.

The Prophet, may Allah bless him and grant him peace, also told us to protect ourselves **'from the evil of what He has created'** (Qur'an: 113.2), by reciting all of the words of Allah (i.e. all of the Qur'an), and by reciting the ayat al-kursi:

> **Allah – there is no god but Him, the Living, the Eternal.**
> **Neither slumber nor sleep overcome Him.**
> **To Him belongs whatever is in the heavens**
> **and whatever is on the earth.**
> **Who is there who can intercede with Him,**
> **except with His permission?**
> **He knows what is in front of them**
> **and what is behind them,**
> **while they encompass nothing of His knowledge**
> **except what He wills.**
> **His seat is the extent of the heavens and the earth,**
> **and He is never weary in preserving them,**
> **and He is the High, the Mighty.**

> **(Qur'an: 2.255)**

'Ayesha, may Allah be pleased with her, said, "When the Prophet, may Allah bless him and grant him peace, was going to bed, he used to put both of his hands together with the palms facing up and blow on them. Then he would recite the surah which begins, **'Say: He is Allah, the One ...'** (Qur'an: 112), and then the two surahs which begin, **'Say: I seek refuge in the Lord ...'** (Qur'an: 113 & 114). Then he would rub as much of his body as he could with his palms, beginning with his head and face and the front of his body." He would do this three times. On this everyone is generally agreed.

Blowing is similar to spitting, but it is without any saliva – for spittle contains saliva. And yet the opposite has been asserted. 'Ayesha, may Allah be pleased with her, was asked about how the

Prophet blew, may Allah bless him and grant him peace, and she replied, "It was like when people spit out raisin pips."

The Prophet, may Allah bless him and grant him peace, said, "Whoever recites the last two ayat of Surat al-Baqara (Qur'an: 2.285-286) at night fall – this will be enough for him." On this there is general agreement. It is also said that this will be enough to give protection from every evil.

The Prophet himself, may Allah bless him and grant him peace, used to say, (before going to sleep), "O Allah, save me from Your punishments on the Day of the Raising of Your slaves," and when he awoke in the morning, he would say, "Praise be to Allah, Who has given us life after death – and to Him we will be raised."

According to a well known hadith, the Prophet, may Allah bless him and grant him peace, told us to seek Allah's forgiveness before going to bed, and to glorify and praise Allah and to exalt Him. He also said, "Whoever recites the ayat al-kursi (Qur'an: 2.255) at bedtime will be covered in the protection of Allah until he awakes." This hadith has been transmitted by al-Bukhari.

Thus the Prophet, may Allah bless him and grant him peace, has pointed us in the direction of reciting these good and blessed and protecting words, instead of seeking protection in fire and pets. It is in this way that he has provided us with protection in this world, by means of these good and blessed words.

And for us there still remains a reward in the next world, which comes to us by our having trusted him, and through his baraka.

The Plague

Usama ibn Zayd asked Sa'd, "What did you hear the Prophet, may Allah bless him and grant him peace, say about the plague?" He replied, "The Prophet, may Allah bless him and grant him peace, said, 'The plague is an impurity which was sent down on the Tribe of Israel and those who were before you. If you hear that the plague is in a place, then do not go there, but if the plague has already arrived and you are there, then do not try to run away from it.'" Al-Bukhari and Muslim have transmitted this hadith.

This hadith, from Anas, is well known: "Dying of the plague is, for all Muslims, to die a martyr." Al-Bukhari and Muslim have transmitted this hadith.

"Dying of the plague is death from pestilence." This is what the author of *Al-Sahah fi'l-Tibb* wrote.

Buboes

'Bubo' is the name given to the fatal swelling caused by the plague which turns black and makes the surrounding areas go green. It usually occurs in the armpits and behind the ears.

Among what has been related by 'Ayesha, may Allah be pleased with her, is this: "A man struck down by the plague is a martyr."

I once asked, "What are the symptoms of someone who has caught the plague?" I was told, "Swollen glands, like a camel's, appearing in the groin and armpits."

Ibn Sina said, "If the eruptions occur in the soft tissue of the armpit, or behind the ear, then it is called the plague." It is caused by corrupted, infected, poisonous blood, often mixed with blood-shot pus, which goes to the heart. Its specific action is fatal. It produces fainting fits and palpitations. The red plague is less dangerous than the yellow plague. The real plague is the black plague, from which no one escapes. It makes pestilence grow worse.

A Commentary on the Words of the Prophet

There are two advantages in obeying the Prophet's command not to go near the plague, may Allah bless him and grant him peace. Firstly, no one will breathe corrupted and infected air and then fall ill. And secondly, no one will go near someone suffering from the plague, and so double the misfortune. That is why there are two commands. It has been transmitted by Abu Daw'ud that the Prophet, may Allah bless him and grant him peace, said, "After contact, destruction follows."

According to Ibn Qutayba, in using the word 'contact', the Prophet, may Allah bless him and grant him peace, was indicating a person's drawing near the plague and pestilence; and his words, '... then do not try to run away from it,' indicate reliance on Allah and trust in Him.

It has also been stated that the Prophet forbade movement towards the pestilence, because movement affects the constitution and weakens the faculties – which is supported by the words of 'Ayesha, may Allah be pleased with her, when she said, "Whenever the Prophet, may Allah bless him and grant him peace, travelled to Madina, he did not feel well." This hadith is from Abu Bakr and Bilal. And if the faculties are weakened, and the constitution affected, then the effects of the pestilential air will be swifter.

As for the words of the Prophet, may Allah bless him and grant him peace, '... if the plague has already arrived and you are there, then do not try to run away from it,' this is because when a devastating disease such as this comes to a land, it weakens everybody and has an effect on all of them, just in the same way that movement weakens all bodies – and so the disaster spreads. And that is the reason for the second part of what the Prophet said.

'Ayesha, may Allah be pleased with her, said, "I asked the Prophet, may Allah bless him and grant him peace, about the plague, and he said, "It is a torture which Allah the Almighty inflicts upon whomever He wishes. And for the believers, Allah has made it a mercy – for once there is an outbreak of the plague in a country, no one will patiently stay there unless he is aware that it will not touch him unless it has been decreed by Allah that his destiny is to die a martyr." This hadith has been transmitted by al-Bukhari.

It should be made clear that 'the plague' and 'the pestilence' are one and the same disease, and that it is a world-wide disease.

What causes the plague is spontaneous putrefaction – like stagnant water, which putrefies as a result of causes either from the earth – for example, from a dead soldier who has not been buried – or from the heavens – for example, very little rain, or a shower of meteorites and stones. When the putrefaction occurs in the air, the humours also putrefy, and then it spreads throughout most of the creation and amongst most people, as far as is possible.

Tenesmus is very painful in this disease. It is said that 20,000 of the Tribe of Israel died from it in one hour, and others say 70,000. It is possible that these were the very first to experience its torments. And when Allah says: **'Have you not considered those who left their homes in their thousands fearing death ...'**, He was referring to the plague.

[Note: According to some commentators, this ayah refers to the flight of the Tribe of Israel with Musa, peace be on him, from Egypt to the Holy Land.]

At-Tamimi said that Sham remained a place of safety from the plague until the last days of Ibn Marwan, especially Damascus and Jordan. It is said that the uncle of as-Saffah was once giving a speech in Damascus, and during it he said, "Allah has been generous towards you all in our time by freeing you from the plague." And one of the audience called out, "Allah is too just to give us both you and the plague!"

According to Jabir ibn 'Atik, there is a well known hadith that there are six kinds of martyrs: the martyr who dies fighting in the way of Allah, the martyr who is struck down by the plague, the martyr who is burned to death, the martyr who dies of pleurisy, the martyr who dies from a disease of the stomach, and the woman who dies a martyr during labour. This hadith has been transmitted by Abu Daw'ud, and is also to be found in the book called *Al-Muwatta'*.

It has been related that 'Abdar-Rahman ibn 'Auf said, "I heard the Prophet, may Allah bless him and grant him peace, say, 'If the pestilence breaks out in a land while you are there, do not leave out of fear, and if you hear that it has broken out in a place, do not go there.'" This hadith has been transmitted by al-Bukhari and Muslim.

The pestilence ebbs and flows. Ibn Sina said, "Whoever wishes to take precautions against the pestilence, should clean all waste moisture from his body. He should go hungry. He should not go to the public baths for a hot bath. He needs to rest, and must keep his humours from becoming agitated." For it is impossible to flee from the plague without movement, and all movement is weakening.

And so the medical meanings flash from the words of the Prophet, may Allah bless him and grant him peace.

The story about 'Umar, may Allah be pleased with him, is well known. When he left for Syria, he had an attack of epilepsy, so he returned to a village in the valley of Tabuk. This is said to be on the borders of the Hijaz, thirteen travelling stages from Madina.

Al-Ghayla (sexual intercourse with a woman who is breast-feeding) and Al-'Azala (coitus interruptus)

It has been related that Asma bint Yazid al-Ansariyya said, "I heard the Prophet, may Allah bless him and grant him peace, say, "Do not kill your children in secrecy, for practising al-ghayla catches the rider and throws him down from his horse." Abu Daw'ud and Ibn Maja transmitted this hadith.

It has been related that Hadama bint Wahab said, "I heard the Prophet, may Allah bless him and grant him peace, say, 'I had in-tended to forbid the practice of al-ghayla, but when I observed the

Romans and the Persians, I saw that their children are subjected to al-ghayla and are not harmed by it at all.'"

Then they asked the Prophet, may Allah bless him and grant him peace, about practising al-'azala, and he replied, "That is killing your children in secrecy, and it is referred to in the ayah, '... **and when the baby girl who was buried alive is asked for what sin she was killed ...'** (Qur'an: 81.8-9). Muslim transmitted this hadith.

A Commentary on the Above Hadith

Imam Malik has stated that the practice of al-ghayla is when a man goes into his wife while she is suckling. A child is said to catch al-ghayl when the mother has intercourse while she is still suckling, and when a woman is suckling and becomes pregnant, her milk is also said to catch al-ghayl. Milk like this will 'throw down' the baby – that is, it will affect it and harm it, because this milk has been corrupted by the waste matter from the menstrual blood. When a woman is pregnant, and when she is suckling, her monthly periods cease. When she is pregnant, the best elements in the blood become food – that is, become nourishment – for the foetus, and the rest – which is the corrupted part – passes to the breasts. Similarly, when she is suckling, all the menstrual blood passes to the breasts and is converted into milk for the nourishment of the baby. And that is why the Prophet, may Allah bless him and grant him peace, said, "Do not kill your children in secrecy ...", for practising al-ghayla 'throws down' the child. In other words, the effects of that corrupted nourishment stay with a man up to puberty and manhood, and if he is challenged to a test of strength in a duel, then he will be overwhelmed in the struggle, because he is weaker than the other man.

As for the words of the Prophet, may Allah bless him and grant him peace, "I had intended to forbid the practice of al-ghayla ...", this prohibition would have been a matter of expediency. In the end, he did not forbid it, because he was aware of the harm that comes to a man from total abstinence and from struggling to control his sexual desire. And he was also aware that the children of the Persians and the Romans were not harmed by it.

As regards the practice of al-'azala, it is halal if both people agree to it.

Jabir said, "We practised withdrawal before ejaculation during the time of the Prophet, may Allah bless him and grant him peace, and the Qur'an permitted this." And Muslim said, "We were practising al-'azala, and when the Prophet, may Allah bless him and grant him peace, came to hear of this, he did not forbid it. Indeed, he also said, 'There is no self that will be reassured on the Day of Rising, that will not be reassured by the fact that this was permitted.'"

'Umar, may Allah be pleased with him, said, "The Prophet, may Allah bless him and grant him peace, forbade the practice of al-'azala with a free woman, unless she consents to it." Ibn Maja has transmitted this hadith.

It is also halal for a woman to take medicine in order to stop the menstrual flow, provided that she is sure that it will not do her any harm. This is the view of Ahmad in his book of sound ahadith. However, there is a group among the followers of Shafi' who reject this, saying that it is haram for her, because it will stop her having children. However, as far as the woman is concerned, that decision rests with the man.

The Evil Eye

The following hadith has been related by Umm Salama: "The Prophet, may Allah bless him and grant him peace, noticed a maid-servant in his house who had a darkness in her face, and the Prophet remarked, 'Leave her alone, for she has the eye in her.'" Al-Bukhari and Muslim have transmitted this hadith.

Please note that when someone says 'the eye', he means 'the evil eye', and that when someone says, 'so-and-so has the eye', he means that so-and-so has been harmed by the look from a jinn.

It has been related by Abu Huraira that the Prophet, may Allah bless him and grant him peace, said, "The evil eye exists." This hadith has been transmitted by al-Bukhari.

The Prophet used to seek protection in Allah for Hassan and Hussayn, may the blessings and peace of Allah be on him and on his family, from every shaytan and all poisons and any evil eye.

Please note that the word 'al-hama' has a plural form 'al-hawam' and means 'everything that is lethally poisonous', like snakes, for example. The word may also be used to describe things which are not fatal, as is demonstrated by his saying, may Allah bless him and grant him peace, to Ka'ab, "Do the insects – 'al-hawam' – hurt you or your head?" And as for the words, 'evil eye' or 'has the evil eye in her', these include any thing which has a bad effect on anyone who looks at it.

'Ayesha, may Allah be pleased with her, has related the hadith that the Prophet, may Allah bless him and grant him peace, used to tell her to recite invocations as a protection against the evil eye. This hadith is agreed on by everyone. This hadith is also from her: "The Prophet, may Allah bless him and grant him peace, told anyone who had been possessed by the evil eye to do wudu, in order to wash away the eye." This has been transmitted by Abu Daw'ud.

It has been related by Ibn 'Abbas that the Prophet, may Allah bless him and grant him peace, said, "The evil eye exists. If anything ever existed before time began, then it was the evil eye. And if you have been possessed by the eye and need a ghusl, then have a ghusl." This hadith has been related by Muslim and at-Tirmidhi.

Isma has given an explanation of his words, may Allah bless him and grant him peace, 'need a ghusl'. It means: If any one of you is struck by the evil eye and asks for water in order to do wudu, then his request should be granted. And whoever is struck by the evil eye should wash his face, his hands, his elbows and knees and the tips of his feet, and what his underwear covers. He should collect the water that he has used in a container and then pour it over the one who possesses the evil eye. Then he should turn the container upside down behind him on the ground. It is said that this pouring the water over him will counteract the effects of the eye, and that he will be cured by the permission of Allah the Almighty. This is what Imam Malik says in his *Al-Muwatta'*.

Ahmad al-Malik was asked, "What does 'what his underwear covers' mean?" He replied, "The parts of the body which are next to the underwear." Abu Daw'ud said, "I asked Ahmad, 'What ayat should be recited as a protection against the evil eye?' He replied, 'It is a question of not being concerned with it.' And he added, 'One group of the commentators on the Qur'an have interpreted this ayah, **'and those who reject almost strike you with their glances ...'** (Qur'an: 68.51), as meaning that they direct the evil eye at you.'"

The Prophet, may Allah bless him and grant him peace, said, "If any one of you sees something that he admires, either in himself or amongst his possessions, then he should ask that it be blessed." And again, he said, "Whoever sees something that he admires, should say, 'Ma sha'Allah – la quwwata ila bi'llah' – 'What Allah wants – there is no power except from Allah'." And it has also been related about him, may Allah bless him and grant him peace, that if he feared that something might be struck by the evil eye, he would say, "May Allah bless it, and may no harm come to it." Also, Abu Sa'id said that the Prophet used to seek refuge in Allah from the jinn and from the evil eye. This has been transmitted by at-Tirmidhi.

Please note that as regards the word 'as-saf'ah' (used in the account about the maid-servant), this means a black mark on the face. Al-Asma'i says that it means a reddish black mark. Ibn Halawia says that 'as-safa'ah' means someone who is mad. In his book on the eye, he defines the disease as displaying both darkness and paleness in the face.

'Ayesha, may Allah be pleased with her, said, "The Prophet, may Allah bless him and grant him peace, permitted people to recite ayat in order to resist the evil eye." Both al-Bukhari and Muslim have transmitted this hadith. According to 'Amran ibn Hasbayni, it has been related in a hadith that he, may Allah bless him and grant him peace, said that all recitations are effective as a remedy against the evil eye and against venom. This has been transmitted by al-Bukhari and Ibn Maja.

Please note that the word used for venom – 'al-hami' – means in this context the poison which comes from any poisonous creature. The sting from a scorpion, or from a wasp, are both called 'al-hami'.

There is an agreed hadith that the Prophet, may Allah bless him and grant him peace, recited some words for a man in pain. It has been related by Anas that the Prophet permitted people to recite ayat against the evil eye, and against venom, and against any rodent ulcer. This has been related by Muslim and Abu Daw'ud. The word used for rodent ulcer – 'an-namlah' – means an ulceration which occurs on the forehead.

Some physicians have incorrectly stated that whoever has the evil eye directs a poisonous energy with his glance which makes contact with the eye of someone else, and thereby inflicts harm. It is said that if the look of some snakes falls on a human being, then that person will die. According to the shari'ah it is said that whoever has the evil eye should do ghusl for the person who has been affected by it. According to the hadith of Ibn Shihab, from Ibn Sahl ibn Hunayf, when the Prophet himself came across it, may Allah bless him and grant him peace, he commanded the man who had the evil eye to do a ghusl and then pour the water from it over the man who had been affected. This has been transmitted by Imam Malik in his *Al-Muwatta'*.

So you should know that reciting ayat and wearing talismans (containing written ayat from the Qur'an) are indeed effective, if they are acceptable to the patient, and accepted by him with his consent as a means of effecting a cure. Reciting ayat and wearing talismans are a form of seeking refuge in Allah in order to protect health, just in the same way that medicine is taken for that purpose. The form of incantations which are blameworthy are those which are not in Arabic and whose meaning is not known – but if the meaning of the words is understood, then the practice is acceptable. It has been related that 'Awf ibn Malik asked about this matter, "Do you mean, 'as we used to do in the days of the jahiliyya'?" And they said, "O Messenger of Allah, what do you say about this?" And he, may Allah bless him and grant him peace, said, "Recite your verses to me." And after he had heard them, he said, "They are all well and good – provided that there is never any suggestion of shirk in them." This account has been transmitted by Muslim.

In another version, it has been related that a man was brought before the Prophet, may Allah bless him and grant him peace, and he said, "O Messenger of Allah, is it true that you have forbidden the recitation of ayat? I once recited an ayah to cure a scorpion sting." And the Prophet replied, "Whoever among you is able to help his brother, should indeed do so." This has been transmitted by Muslim.

So what is not permitted is the use of magical charms – or perhaps it could be said that once the prohibition was absolute, but then it was later modified.

I once asked Abu 'Abdullah about reciting words as a protection against scorpions. He saw no harm in the practice, provided that the meaning of the words was understood, or that they were from the Qur'an.

Shifa bint 'Abdullah said, "The Prophet, may Allah bless him and grant him peace, entered the tent while I was there with Hafsa, and he said to me, 'Teach her the talismans for protection against herpes,' – in the same way that I had taught her to write." Abu Daw'ud has transmitted this. It will also be noted that this hadith informs us that women are permitted to be taught how to write.

This hadith comes from 'Ayesha, may Allah be pleased with her: "Whenever people used to come and complain about something like an ulcer or a wound, the Prophet, may Allah bless him and grant him peace, would put his forefinger in the dust, and then he would raise it and say, 'In the Name of Allah, when the dust of our earth is mixed with the spittle of some of us, it will cure our sick, by the permission of our Lord.'" There is general agreement about this hadith.

The words 'dust of our earth' were used because the constitution of dust is cold and dry, and it acts as a desiccant for anything that is wet. Now, ulcers and wounds contain a great deal of wetness within them, which prevents the faculties from functioning properly, which in turn hinders swift healing. And as for the words 'the spittle of some of us' – that is, our saliva – this means that if some saliva is mixed with dust and allowed to dry, and this is then applied to ulcers or wounds, then they will heal, by the permission of Allah. There are many ahadith on this subject.

As regards reciting ayat from the Qur'an, it has been related that 'Ali, may Allah be pleased with him, said, "The best medicine is the Qur'an." At-Tirmidhi has transmitted this hadith.

Allah the Almighty says:

We have revealed in the Qur'an that which is a healing and a mercy to the believers ...

(Qur'an: 17.82)

The word 'in' does not refer to certain parts only, but the meaning is that everything which has been revealed in the Qur'an heals. The Qur'an heals physical diseases, if it is used for that purpose, just as it cures error, ignorance, and doubt. It gives guidance to whoever is lost and bewildered; it cures the heart by removing ignorance from it; and it heals the body by removing sickness from it. You should realise that healthy bodies belong to healthy hearts. If you make sure your heart is healthy, then your body will also be healthy. The Prophet, may Allah bless him and grant him peace, said, "There is in the body a lump of flesh, and if this lump of flesh is healthy, then the whole body will be healthy ..." This is a hadith.

We have already discussed using recitation from the Qur'an as a remedy. 'Ayesha said, "Whenever any member of the Prophet's household was sick, he used to recite the last two surahs of the Qur'an over him or her."

A hadith has been transmitted by Dar Qatni in his *Compendium of Authorities*, which states, quoting Ibn 'Abbas, that the Prophet, may Allah bless him and grant him peace, said, "Whoever suffers from toothache should put his finger on the tooth and recite the ayah, **'And He is the One Who has brought you into being from a single self, and (has given you) a place to stay and a place of rest: We have indeed made the signs clear for people who understand.'** (Qur'an: 6.98)."

If some words have been given special properties, and are beneficial by the permission of Allah, then what do you think about the actual words of Allah the Almighty Himself? Ahmad wrote: "If words from the Qur'an are written down on something, and then washed off, and then what has been washed off is drunk, that is all well and good. Again, if someone writes down a passage from the Qur'an, and then puts it inside a container, and then tells a sick person to drink from it – or even if he only recites something from the Qur'an over the container, and then the sick person drinks from it – this too is well and good. Similarly, if someone recites something from the Qur'an over some water, and then sprinkles this water over a sick person – or in the case of a difficult labour, if someone writes something down from the Qur'an, and then makes the woman drink it – all this is well and good."

It has been related by Ibn 'Abbas, "If a woman finds difficulty in giving birth, she should take a clean container and write the following ayat inside it:

... On the Day when they see what they were promised,
it will seem as if they had only lingered there
for an hour of the day ...

(Qur'an: 46.35)

and also this:

On the Day when they see it,
it will seem as if they had only lingered there
for an evening or a morning.

(Qur'an: 79.46)

and also this ayah:

**There is certainly a lesson in their story
for people who have understanding ...**

(Qur'an: 12.111)"

This writing should then be dissolved in water, and the woman given the mixture to drink, as well as having some of it poured over her abdomen.

According to the *Ahadith of Muhanna*, Ahmad once gave a fatwa that it is halal to free someone who has been bewitched from the spell by using any form of medicine, and that it is quite possible to break a magical spell. For when the Prophet, may Allah bless him and grant him peace, had a spell put on him, he repelled it and freed himself, and this freeing himself was accomplished through using medicine.

In everyday language, the word 'spell' means effecting a change in the form of a thing. Thus when we say, 'What has bewitched you like this?', we mean, 'What has brought about this change in you?'

The word 'spell' is also used to describe being completely fooled – while, on the other hand, the one who makes the spell may be a very clever person.

Now, spells may take the form of amulets containing written verses, or spells that are woven, or words that are spoken over a person by a spell binder, or words written down by him – by which means an effect is produced in the body of the person who has been bewitched, or in his heart, or indirectly through his mind. In fact by these means, a man can be killed, or be made to fall ill, or even separated from his womenfolk. Magic can indeed come between a man and his wife, and make them hate each other, and destroy their love for each other.

'Ayesha, may Allah be pleased with her, said, "I once used to imagine that the Prophet, may Allah bless him and grant him peace, had done something which he had not in fact done. I seek refuge in Allah from this, and His mercy."

It was once said to Ahmad: "Physicians maintain that nothing can enter a human being – meaning by that, any of the inhabitants of the earth." He replied. "That is sheer nonsense, for the Prophet, may Allah bless him and grant him peace, said, 'Truly shaytan runs inside a human being just as his blood runs inside him.'" However, I – the author of this book – maintain that the bodies of the jinn are subtle bodies, and that it is impossible for the humours of the jinn to mingle with the human self in the same way that, in human bodies, blood and phlegm mingle, along with all their impurities.

When news of 'Umar was late in reaching Abu Musa, he went to a woman who had a shaytan in her belly. He asked her about 'Umar, and she replied, "I will tell you when my shaytan has given me the answer." When he came, she put the question to him, and the shaytan replied, "When I left him, he was preparing some camels to give away as sadaqa."

This subject is a very diverse one, and there are many stories – far too many to record in this book! And Allah knows everything.

Wearing Amulets

Ahmad wrote that wearing amulets is extremely disliked. He said, "Whoever wears an amulet comes to depend on it." It has been related by Harab that he once discussed this matter with Ahmad: "I said, 'Is there anything in the Qur'an, or anywhere else, about wearing amulets?' And Ahmad replied, 'Ibn Mas'ud hated them.' He also quoted the words of 'Ayesha, may Allah be pleased with her, and of some other women, saying that they did not oppose this practice. Ahmad himself was far from being strict about it."

The following hadith has come from 'Abdullah ibn 'Umar: "If any one of you suffers from sleeplessness, he should say, 'I seek refuge in the perfect words of Allah from His anger, and from His punishment, and from the evil of His slaves, and from the whisperings of the shayatin, and from their presence.' These words will certainly not fail you."

'Abdullah ibn 'Umar used to teach these words to his children when they were growing up, and while they were still young, he would write them down as a text and hang it round their necks. Abu Daw'ud and at-Tirmidhi have transmitted this hadith. These are his very words – and at-Tirmidhi has commented, "This is strange, but it is true." This hadith has also been transmitted by an-Nasa'i in his *Al-Yawm wa'l-Layla*.

As regards the view that the use of amulets is abhorrent and should be avoided, the justification for this depends on the degree to which trust is placed in their intrinsic power to do good or harm, and the degree to which the words are not understood – and we have already discussed this above. (See pages 132 to 134, and also 158 to 159).

As regards the technique of effecting healing by using recitation, which is known as 'an-nushra' – that is, when verses are recited over some water, which is then left out and used by a sick person for washing himself – Ahmad used to say, "Ibn Mas'ud hated that."

Abu Daw'ud said in his book called *Kitab al-Marasil bi Ishnadihi*: "I asked al-Hassan about the practice of using such charms, and he replied, 'The Prophet, may Allah bless him and grant him peace, told me that this is from the work of shaytan.'" And the same hadith has been related by Jabir.

Spiritual Remedies

Abu Huraira said, "The Prophet, may Allah bless him and grant him peace, saw me while I was trying to sleep, and I was writhing about with a pain in my stomach. He said, 'Is your stomach giving you pain?' and I answered, 'Yes, O Messenger of Allah.' And then he said, 'Get up and pray, for truly there is healing in the prayer.'" This has been transmitted by Ibn Maja.

Please note that the words that the Prophet used, may Allah bless him and grant him peace, were in Persian, meaning, 'Do you have a pain in your stomach?' The Persian word 'shikam' is the same as the Arabic word 'batan', and 'dard' is the same as 'waja''.

As regards the above hadith, the wise say that there are two things to be learnt from it. The first is that the Prophet, may Allah bless him and grant him peace, could speak Persian, and the second is that the prayer cures pain in the heart, in the stomach, and in the bowels.

In the same way, we can deduce three principles: Firstly, there is the divine command to worship Allah. Secondly, there is a psychological aspect to this – that is, that the one who is suffering will forget about his pain while he is praying, so that the intensity of the pain will diminish, until finally his energy will overcome the pain and remove it altogether. And thirdly, it shows us that the best doctor is the one who uses every kind of tactic in order to strengthen the faculties. At one point he will increase strength through food, and at another, by provoking joy and grief, or even hope and fear. And prayer is the best of them all. If a person is engaged in worship, then he will experience apprehension, fear, hope, uncertainty, and love. And when his attention turns to the next life, it will strengthen his faculties, delight his heart, and, by these very means, drive out disease.

It has been related from some source that a child of 'Ali, may Allah be pleased with him, once had an abscess. No one dared to make the incision that was needed. So his family let him go to do the prayer – and then they were able to make the incision, for he was so absorbed in the prayer that he did not pay them any attention!

Abu Ayyub used to tell his family to keep quiet in the house when he was there – but when he was doing the prayer, he used to permit conversation, saying, "I cannot hear you talking while I am doing the prayer." Once a wall of the mosque fell down while he was doing the prayer, and it did not even distract him!

Doing the prayer is something natural, as it benefits both the mind and the body – for it includes standing, bowing, and prostrating, as well as being still, tranquillity, piety, worship, submission, abasement of the self, and other elements. Thanks to all this, the joints of the body are moved and relaxed, as well as most of the organs – and especially the stomach and the bowels. How powerful the effect of all these things is in helping to move the two impurities (urine and faeces) along, and to speed up the departure of food from the stomach.

Al-Muwaffaq 'Abdal-Latif said in his book called *Kitab al-Arba'in*: "I once saw a group of idle, common, people who were nevertheless all enjoying good health, so I made enquiries as to why this was so, and learned that they often prayed, and that they did the prayer at night especially – so finally I said to myself, 'How very beneficial prostrating is for those who suffer from colds and catarrh!'"

Indeed prostrating is most effective in clearing the nasal passages when they are blocked, and how beneficial prostrating is in helping to expel the two impurities by speeding up the passage of food from the stomach and the bowels, and in moving waste matter along with it, until it is expelled – for in some stomachs there is food piled up on food, and one meal falls upon the one that was eaten before it. Furthermore, doing the prayer often gives pleasure to the one who is doing it, as well as expelling bad thoughts and putting out the fire of anger. Doing the prayer makes one humble before Allah and tolerant of others. Doing the prayer softens the heart, and it makes forgiveness treasured and revenge abhorrent to a person.

It often happens that while doing the prayer, a correct opinion surfaces, and the way to conduct one's affairs properly, or a well-considered answer, become apparent. Often a worshipper remembers during the prayer what he had forgotten earlier. Doing the prayer makes a person reflect on his beginning and on his end, and on how he stands in this world, and in the next. It will remind him of his own reckoning, especially if he stands in prayer for a long time, and especially during the night – when eyes are lowered, and voices are hushed, and the influence of the lower world is weakened, and the thirst of the flocks has been quenched, and the influence of the world of the spirits is greater, and gloomy thoughts are transformed into joyful ones. This is what the Prophet meant, may Allah bless him and grant him peace, when he said, "O Bilal, let us take rest in prayer!" And again, when he said, "I find my comfort in doing the prayer, because it is from this that a person is given pleasure, and the pleasure that comes from it brings comfort – and because doing the prayer contains all that is excellent in both this world and the next."

We have already quoted the hadith of the Prophet, may Allah bless him and grant him peace, "Digest your food with the Name of Allah and with conversation about Him." This is one of the reasons why the tarawih prayer is customary.

So it is from the prayer that the best of this world and of the next is derived. It is from the prayer that strength, which flows from the blessed vision of Allah, the Creator, springs – and that is why doing the prayer drives out everything to do with sickness and illness from the body, and reveals a person's true nature to him, so that he strives to perfect what is already good, and to abandon whatever is bad.

Sahil ibn Sa'd has related this: "The Prophet, may Allah bless him and grant him peace, spat into the eye of 'Ali, may Allah be pleased with him, when he was suffering from ophthalmia, and asked for Allah's blessing on him – and 'Ali was cured." Al-Bukhari and Muslim have transmitted this hadith.

Indeed this section falls short in describing the virtues of prayer. And Allah knows best.

It is said that a man complained to the Prophet, may Allah bless him and grant him peace, about having pain in his eyes, and the Prophet replied, "Rest your gaze on the Holy Book."

It is said that a certain man complained to the Prophet, may Allah bless him and grant him peace, about the hardness of his own heart, and the Prophet replied, "Stroke the head of an orphan, and give him something to eat." The same complaint was once made to Abu Daw'ud, who said, "Visit the sick, go to funerals, and visit tombs."

Al-Maruzi said, "It has been related by Ahmad, 'I once had a fever and a man wrote the following talisman as a protection against fever for me: **"In the Name of Allah, the Merciful, the Compassionate** (Qur'an: 1.1) – by the Name of Allah – by Allah Himself – and I bear witness that Muhammad is the Messenger of Allah – **'O fire, be coolness and peace on Ibrahim'** – **and they wanted to trap him, but We made them the greater losers** (Qur'an: 21.69-70) – O Lord of Jibril, Mikail and Rafail, cure whoever possesses this writing by Your might and by Your power and by Your strength – O Lord of the creation – Amin – So be it."'"

'Uthman ibn Abi al-'Asi said, "A man complained to the Prophet, may Allah bless him and grant him peace, of a pain that he had felt in his body ever since he had embraced Islam, and the Prophet said to him in reply, 'Put your right hand on the place where the pain is, and say, seven times, "I seek refuge in the power of Allah and in His might from the evil that I find and feel."'" Muslim has transmitted this hadith.

Khalid ibn al-Walid said, "O Messenger of Allah, I cannot sleep at night because of my insomnia," and the Prophet, may Allah bless him and grant him peace, replied, "When you go to your bed to sleep, then say, 'O Allah, Lord of the seven heavens and whatever they cover, and Lord of the seven earths and whatever they contain, and Lord of the shayatin and whomever they mislead, be my Protector against all the evils of Your creation if any one of them oppresses me or overwhelms me. Whoever is protected by You is made powerful, and blessed is Your Name. There is no god other than You, and there is no god except You.'" At-Tirmidhi has transmitted this hadith.

Please note that the word 'insomnia' means an inability to sleep.

It is said that Dhalid complained to the Prophet, may Allah bless him and grant him peace, of nightmares, and the Prophet replied, "Shall I teach you some words which Jibril taught me? : 'I seek refuge in the face of Allah, the Generous, and in the perfect words of Allah – more than which no man can do, whether he is good or bad – and I seek protection from the evil which comes down from the heavens and displays itself there, and from the evil which is on the earth, and from the evil of temptations in the day and in the night, and from the evil of misfortunes in the day and in the night, and from everything except whatever brings a blessing with it, O Merciful One!'" This has been transmitted by at-Tabari.

A Prescription for a Tonic to Make the Heart Peaceful and Drive Away Anxiety

This is made up from a mixture of only eating whatever is halal, and being scrupulous in one's obedience, and avoiding whatever is makruh, and restraining the outward display of all negative thoughts, and keeping one's inner feelings under control, and ruling one's self with wisdom, and carefully keeping secrets, and humbly asking Allah – may He be praised and exalted – for protection against the evils of one's own desires and one's own shaytan.

Bilal said, "These evils are taken away from you through your worshipping Allah at night, for this was the custom of the good people who came before you, and it prevents wrong action and brings you near to Allah. It wipes out wrong actions and it expels disease from the body." This hadith has been transmitted by at-Tirmidhi.

Another Prescription

It is said that one day Dhu'n-Nun walked past some doctors. They were surrounded by a lot of people, both men and women, who were holding bottles of urine in their hands. The doctors were writing out prescriptions for all of them, each in accordance with the disease which each person had.

Dhu'n-Nun said, "I approached one of the doctors and greeted him, and he returned my greeting. Then I said to him, 'May Allah have mercy on you – please give me the remedy for wrong action.' The doctor kept his head lowered for an hour, and then raised it and said, 'If I prescribe a remedy for you, will you give me your attention and understanding?' And I replied, 'Yes, insh'Allah.'

"Then the doctor said, 'Take the root of poverty mixed with the pollen of patience, and the myrobalan of submission, and the belleric of remembrance of Allah, along with the tamarind of humility, the polypody of sincerity, the rhubarb of purity, and the agaric of faithfulness. Put all of these into a pot which is free of wrong action, and then light the fire of devotion beneath it, until the bubbles of wisdom rise to the surface. When these bubbles appear, pour them through the sieve of remembrance, and strain them into the cup of acceptance. Fan this with the fan of the praise of Allah, until it is cool. When it is cool, then drink it, and taste the doing without that is in it. After that you will never commit any wrong action.'"

So, treat your heart with these remedies, just as you treat your body with those medicines, and by this means you will enjoy a complete and perfect restoration to health, both in this world and in the next.

And truly there is no power except from Allah, the High, the Mighty.

The Benefits in Being Sick and in Visiting the Sick

Truly sickness is one of the strongest incentives to make a believer turn to Allah in repentance, and speak truthfully, and make amends for his wrong actions, and direct himself towards the Garden.

It has been related that the Prophet, may Allah bless him and grant him peace, said, "Whoever dies on a sick-bed, dies the death of a martyr and is safe from the questioning in the grave. His provision comes to him as provision from the Garden." This is what Ibn Maja has transmitted.

Abu Huraira and Abu Sa'id have related that the Prophet, may Allah bless him and grant him peace, said, "A believer does not suffer from any sickness, or fatigue, or trouble, or even sorrow that causes him anxiety, or a thorn that pricks his skin, without Allah forgiving him his wrong actions on account of this." This has been transmitted by al-Bukhari and Muslim.

It has been related that the Prophet, may Allah bless him and grant him peace, said, "Truly a believer should not fear sickness, for if he knew of the benefits that come from being sick, he would want to be sick even until he died." This hadith has been related by az-Zar.

The Prophet, may Allah bless him and grant him peace, said, "Most of the martyrs in my community are those who died in bed." As for those who died in the battle of Siffin, only Allah knows what was in their hearts. This has been related by Ibn Abi Shabayba.

A hadith which has been related by Jabir states: "Truly fever removes the wrong actions of the Tribe of Adam just as bellows help to remove the impurities from iron." Abu Huraira adds that the Prophet, may Allah bless him and grant him peace, also said, "If Allah intends a blessing for someone, He will make him taste it." This has been transmitted by al-Bukhari.

'Ayesha, may Allah be pleased with her, said, "I have not seen anyone in any pain greater than what I have seen in the Prophet, may Allah bless him and grant him peace." Al-Bukhari has transmitted this hadith.

The Prophet, may Allah bless him and grant him peace, said, "The people who experience the most suffering are the prophets of Allah, and then the awliya, and then the salihin. A man is afflicted in proportion to his love of the deen. Affliction does not cease for the awliya as long as they walk on this earth and until they have been purified from wrong action." This hadith has been transmitted by at-Tirmidhi, and it is a reliable and sound hadith.

The Prophet, may Allah bless him and grant him peace, said, "If Allah loves a people, he gives them affliction."

The Prophet, may Allah bless him and grant him peace, said, "There is no sickness or pain which a believer experiences that is not a purification of his wrong actions – whether it is a thorn which pricks him, or a disaster which overwhelms him." Al-Bukhari has transmitted this hadith.

The Prophet, may Allah bless him and grant him peace, said, "No Muslim experiences any harm without Allah stripping away his wrong actions from him, like a tree which sheds its leaves." There are many other similar ahadith like this one which have been transmitted.

The Prophet, may Allah bless him and grant him peace, said, "If there had been nothing else for the Tribe of Adam but safety and health, this would have been enough for them." This hadith has been transmitted by Abu Daw'ud.

Ath-Thawar said, "After recovering my good health, I find that my eyesight has deteriorated. Is it not enough, after an illness, to be safe and well again?"

When Abu 'Abbas was an old man, he was once asked how he was. He replied, "I am suffering from the disease which everyone wants to have!"

'Umru ibn Qamayt said:

> My back never grew weak from standing up,
> only from the passing days, day and night.
> Greedily I asked Allah for good health,
> and He gave me safety.

And so there is the saying:

> O My slave, good health makes a connection
> between you and your self,
> while sickness makes a connection
> between you and Me.

A person should indeed ask Allah for good health, but if Allah gives him sickness, then it should be received with patience, and with acceptance, and with gratitude.

Al-Harith al-Majasi said, "Affliction is a punishment for troublemakers, a purification for those who turn to Allah in repentance, and a mark of honour for the pure in heart."

The Prophet, may Allah bless him and grant him peace, said, "Visit the sick and free slaves."

The Prophet, may Allah bless him and grant him peace, said, "Whoever visits the sick, or visits his brother in the deen, will have his virtue made known and his behaviour praised, and a high station in the Garden will be reserved for him." This hadith has been transmitted by at-Tirmidhi.

The Prophet, may Allah bless him and grant him peace, said, "A visit to a sick person is only complete when one of you has put his hand on his forehead and asked him how he is." This hadith has been transmitted by at-Tirmidhi. According to another version, the visitor should put his hand on the sick person and say, "How did last night go for you?" or, "How has today been for you?"

According to Anas, the Prophet, may Allah bless him and grant him peace, only used to visit a sick person after he had been ill for three days. Ibn Maja has transmitted this.

The Prophet, may Allah bless him and grant him peace, said, "Whenever you enter the house of someone who is sick, remind him of the end that has been decreed for him." This also has been transmitted by Ibn Maja.

The Prophet, may Allah bless him and grant him peace, said, "Whoever visits a sick man is walking along the high road to the Garden." This has been transmitted by al-Bukhari.

Whenever the Prophet, may Allah bless him and grant him peace, entered the house of a sick man, he used to put his hand on him and say, "All is well and good: may this be a means of purification, insh'Allah." This has been transmitted by al-Bukhari.

According to Abu Huraira, the Prophet, may Allah bless him and grant him peace, made three exceptions, who should not be visited: whoever is suffering from ophthalmia, from deafness, and from boils.

The Prophet, may Allah bless him and grant him peace, said to 'Umar, may Allah be pleased with him, "If you enter the room of a sick person, then ask him to pray to Allah for you – for the supplication of a sick person is like the supplication of the angels."

The Prophet, may Allah bless him and grant him peace, said, "If you enter the house of a sick man, then only speak good words, for truly the angels will confirm what you say, and they will open up the way to the Garden for him."

The Prophet, may Allah bless him and grant him peace, said, "Whoever visits a sick person, whose predestined hour has not yet come, and says, seven times, 'I ask Allah, the Great, the Lord of the Mighty Throne, to cure you,' then Allah will certainly restore his health."

It was the custom of the Prophet, may Allah bless him and grant him peace, whenever he visited the sick, or if a sick person was brought to him, to say, "O Allah, take away this illness. O Lord of mankind, heal this, for You are the Healer. There is no cure, except from You – a cure which leaves no illness behind." After this, a person who is sick should recite the opening surah of the Qur'an to himself, and then he should recite the surah which begins, **'Say: He is Allah – He is One ...'** (Qur'an: 112.1), and then finally the last two surahs. Then he should blow on the palms of his hands and rub his face and body. This has been described in the book called *As-Sahih* as being the sunnah of the Prophet, may Allah bless him and grant him peace.

A person who is sick should also repeat the supplication for satisfying a need, which goes: 'There is no god except Allah the Great, the Merciful – there is no god except Allah, the Lord of the Mighty Throne – there is no god except Allah, the Lord of the heavens and the earth, and the Lord of the Throne of Mercy.'

It is alright for a sick person to say, "O, my pain is terrible!" The Prophet, may Allah bless him and grant him peace, used to say, "O my head, O my head!"

A person who is sick should not display either fear or displeasure, and should say, "Praise and thanks to Allah!", before expressing any complaints – and then they will cease to be complaints.

It is quite alright for the relatives of a sick person to ask his physician about him. Whenever 'Ali, may Allah be pleased with him, used to leave the presence of the Prophet when he was ill, may Allah bless him and grant him peace, people used to ask about him, and 'Ali would say something like, "He had a good night and is better, praise and thanks to Allah."

It is not good for a person who is sick to long for death, but if he is afraid that he might lose his iman, then it is permissible.

'Ayesha, may Allah be pleased with her, said, "I saw the Prophet, may Allah bless him and grant him peace, at the time when his death was near. There was a cup of water next to him. He put his hand into the cup and then wiped his face with it. Then he said, "O Allah, help me with the pain of death and its agonies." She also added that he said, "O Allah, forgive me and have mercy on me, and join me with the highest company." This hadith is generally agreed.

Shaykh Muhiyu'd-Din said, in his book called *Kitab al-Adhkara*, "It is advisable for anyone who thinks he has not long to live to spend a lot of time reciting the Qur'an and remembering Allah. It is most improper for him to be afraid, or bad-tempered, or quarrelsome, or abusive, or argumentative about anything that is not to do with protecting the deen. He should be aware that these are the last hours of his life in this world. He should strive to end it well, and try to fulfil all his obligations, return what has been entrusted to him, and pay off all his debts. He should forgive his relatives, his children, his servants, his neighbours and friends, and all those with whom he has done business. He should be thankful to Allah the Almighty, with acceptance and having a good opinion of Him, hoping that He will have mercy on him and forgive him – and then Allah may let him off the punishment that he deserves, and the worship that is still owing."

So the sick man should ask Allah for forgiveness and pardon. He should ask for verses which inspire hope, and sayings which inspire confidence, and stories about the awliya, to be read to him. He should settle his affairs concerning his children. He should remind himself of the words of various prayers, and he should avoid all less important things. He should take particular care not to fail in this respect, for the worst possible thing is to end one's life in this world while being forgetful of what is due to Allah. He should not pay any attention to the words of anyone who tries to deceive him about this matter – for someone like this may indeed approach him.

It is advisable for a dying man to ask his relatives to be patient with him during his sickness, and to bear their own distress with patience. He should do his best to tell them not to weep over him, and he should remind them of the truth of the words of the Prophet, may Allah bless him and grant him peace, who once said, "The dead are punished as much as the weeping of their relatives over them." So the person who is sick should say, "O my dear friends, please stop doing what will bring punishment down on me." And they for their part should do what he asks. He should also ask them not to raise their voices when they are reciting the Qur'an for him and carrying out the other funeral rites.

When the sick person is drawing his last breath, he should repeat, over and over again, "There is no god except Allah," and he should say to whoever is with him, "If I forget to do this, please remind me of it." Truly the Prophet, may Allah bless him and grant him peace, said, "Whoever makes his last words, **'There is no god except Allah'**, will surely enter the Garden." This hadith has been transmitted by Abu Daw'ud.

The Prophet, may Allah bless him and grant him peace, also said, "Teach your people to say, when they are dying, 'There is no god except Allah'." This has been transmitted by Muslim.

If a person who is dying is not repeating these words, one of those who are present should remind him – but very gently, in case he becomes angry and refuses to say them. And if he says them even once, then do not make him repeat them again, unless different words are going to be used. If he does not say them quite right, do not contradict him, in case the dying man dies while he is still being corrected.

When the eyes of the dying man close for the last time, then say, "In the Name of Allah and in the deen of the Prophet, may Allah bless him and grant him peace," and do not say anything except good, for the angels will confirm everything that is said. It has been related in a hadith that al-Ansari used to recite Surat'al-Baqara (Qur'an: 2) in the presence of a dying person. Another hadith states that Surah Ya Sin (Qur'an: 36) used to be recited over the dying. This has been transmitted by Abu Daw'ud.

Something made of iron should be placed on the abdomen of a dying person. When 'Umar ibn al-Khattab reached his last moment, may Allah be pleased with him, he said to his son, "Put my cheek next to the ground," and then he wept until the mud stuck to his eyelashes, because of his numerous tears – and all the time he was saying, "Woe to 'Umar, and woe to his mother, if Allah does not overlook his wrong actions." In another version of this account, it says that 'Umar's weeping made everyone around him weep too.

And this is what he said when he died, may Allah be pleased with him: "I would give away everything that I possess – I, upon whom the sun will never rise again – in order to avoid the fear (of what will happen to me) after it has risen." And he said to his sons, "When you put me into my grave, then put my cheek on the earth, so that there is nothing between my cheek and the earth." And he said to Hafsa, his daughter, may Allah be pleased with her, "Swear by what you will inherit from me that you will not mourn for me, for – although you may not have any control over what comes from your eyes – truly no one is ever mourned for virtues that he never possessed, without incurring the hatred of the angels."

After he had died, may Allah be pleased with him, this righteous man was seen in a dream, and he was asked, "What happened to you?", to which he replied, "All is well – my body would have almost certainly been sent to the Fire, had I not found my Lord Merciful and Forgiving."

When 'Umar ibn 'Abd al-Aziz was on his death-bed, he said, "I would not like the pangs of death to be eased, for they give a Muslim his last chance to earn a reward. Later, he was seen in a dream, and was asked what deeds he had found were most excellent, to which he replied, "Asking for forgiveness."

When his death was approaching, Ibn Mu'adh said, "Welcome, O death, my invisible visitor. O my friend, you have come just when I needed you. O Allah, how I used to fear You – but now I ask for Your mercy."

During the illness from which he died, a well-known person said, "When I die, then give away my garments – for naked I came into this world, and naked I wish to leave it."

Abu Bakr said, "I was with al-Junayd when he died. He recited the entire Qur'an, and then started again from Surat'al-Baqara (Qur'an: 2). He had reached the seventieth ayah, when he died, may Allah the Almighty have mercy on him."

Embryology and Anatomy

One of my brothers asked me to tell him something about human anatomy, and how food reaches the various organs – so I answered his question, placing my trust in Allah, and saying as follows:

Allah the Almighty says:

Certainly We created man from a mixture of clay;
then We made him a drop in a secure resting-place;
then We formed the drop into a clot;
then We formed the clot into a lump of flesh;
then We gave the lump of flesh bones;
then We clothed the bones with flesh;
and then We brought it into being as a new creation.
So blessed is Allah, the Best of Creators.
And then surely, after this, you die.
And then surely on the Day of Resurrection,
you will be raised again.

(Qur'an: 23.12-16)

Please note that the words of Allah, 'Certainly We created man' refer to the creation of the Tribe of Adam. The word 'man', being both singular and plural, means all of them – all of whom derive from the original mixture of clay (from which Adam was formed, peace be on him).

Ibn 'Abbas said, "The 'mixture of clay' indicates the very essence." Muhammad, may Allah bless him and grant him peace, said, "It means the semen of the sons of Adam." 'Akrama stated that it means the fluid which comes from the loins.

As for the word 'drop', the Arabs describe the drop as the mixture of clay, and its originator as the One Who mixed it, or Who makes it flow – because both the mixture and the drop flow from the clay from which Adam was created, peace be on him.

It is also said that the meaning of the word 'man' is Adam, and that His words 'mixture of clay' or 'flow' imply a mixture of all kinds of clay. Al-Kalabi adds that the drop flowed from the clay, and that the clay was Adam, peace be on him.

So then, 'We made him a drop' – that is, man – and placed him 'in a secure resting place' which is firmly protected – that is, the uterus, which is concealed and which is a secure resting place for the drop until it has grown to maturity.

Next, 'We formed the drop into a clot'. It is said that there is an interval of forty days between the two creations. Ibn Mas'ud has related, "The Prophet, may Allah bless him and grant him peace – and he is the most trustworthy of those who know – told us that it was decreed that everything in creation should take forty days to form in the womb of its mother. And so the clot is like that."

Next comes 'the lump of flesh', in a similar period of time. Then Allah sends an angel to breathe a soul into it, and He has commanded that (at this point) its destiny is to be written with regard to four matters – that is, its means of livelihood, its life span, its actions, and whether it will be happy or unhappy. This is from the hadith that has been transmitted by al-Bukhari and by Muslim.

Physicians are agreed that the foetus is initially created in the uterus, and that it rests there for about forty days. It is at this point that the male and female elements are differentiated, depending on the heat of the temperaments and the faculties. Next comes the clot of blood, in a similar period of time, and this clot is like a piece of congealed blood. Then comes the lump of flesh, in a similar period of time – or you could describe it as a small piece of tissue – and so this is at the end of the third period of forty days.

It is then that it begins to move, for as the Prophet, may Allah bless him and grant him peace, stated, its soul is breathed into it at this point. All the people of knowledge are agreed that no soul is breathed into it until after the fourth month.

So you should know that semen is milky to begin with, looking like scum on water, and then it becomes bloody, and finally, fleshy. Then it is given a form, and then it begins to move.

The shortest possible period for a pregnancy – after which the child can survive – is 182 days, (26 weeks). Full term pregnancy lasts 280 days, (40 weeks).

Ibn 'Abbas has related the hadith that the fluid of a man is white and thick, and that the fluid of a woman is thin and yellow. The family resemblance of a child depends on whichever of these two fluids is more subtle or more fine.

Muslim has transmitted the hadith that the main organs and the bones come from the man's fluid, and that the flesh comes from the woman's fluid.

It has been related by Anas that 'Abdullah ibn Salam once asked the Prophet, may Allah bless him and grant him peace, how it is that a child either resembles his father or his mother, and the Prophet replied, "If the fluid of the man exceeds that of the woman, then the child will resemble the father, but if the fluid of the woman exceeds that of the man, then the child will resemble her."

It has been transmitted by al-Bukhari that a man's fluid is hot and strong, and therefore thick and white, whereas a woman's fluid is thinner and weaker, and therefore yellow. Whether the child will resemble one parent rather than the other, depends on how much fluid is emitted, which fluid exceeds the other fluid, and whose sexual appetite is the stronger.

Hippocrates said, "Semen flows from every organ, and from the healthy man comes healthy semen, and from the diseased, diseased. The Prophet, may Allah bless him and grant him peace, said, "The possibility of becoming junub lies beneath every single hair." His words 'beneath every single hair' indicate the same fact – that is, that semen flows from every organ.

Then come the words of Allah the Almighty, 'and then We brought it into being as a new creation' (Qur'an: 23.14). Ibn 'Abbas, al-Mujahid, 'Akrama, ash-Sha'bi, adh-Dhahak and Abu 'Aliyah all said, "This refers to the soul being breathed into it."

Al-Qatada said, "The blossoming of man is the appearance of pubic hair." Al-Mujahid added, "It is the point of maturity in youth." And al-Hassan also added, "Whether it is a man or a woman."

It has been related by al-'Awfi, from Ibn 'Abbas, "The growth of pubic hair indicates a major transition in status after birth: A person waits, from the time of sexual intercourse until birth, until the time of sitting up, until the time of standing up, until walking, until being weaned, until the time of eating and drinking, until reaching puberty, until the time of rising up through society – and until the time of everything that goes with that." All of this is discussed in the various commentaries.

So, may Allah be praised, may He be glorified, and may He be thanked for all that He has been and still is – the Best of creators, and of designers, and of those who decree.

Now then, in terms of design, 'creation' indicates man. Allah, the Creator, is also the Designer. Al-Mujahid said, "And so they were designed – and it was Allah Who designed them."

'Ayesha, may Allah be pleased with her, said, "The Prophet, may Allah bless him and grant him peace, once said to 'Ali, may Allah be pleased with him, "All of mankind, from the Tribe of Adam, have each been created with 360 joints. Whoever says, 'Allah is Greatest', or 'Blessed is Allah', or 'Glory to Allah', or 'may Allah Forgive me'; or whoever removes a stone from the pathway, or a thorn, or a bone; or whoever calls people to what is good, and forbids what is bad – whoever does any of these things as many times as there are 360 joints, will be protected from the fire of Hell on that Day, and will have saved his soul." Muslim has transmitted this hadith.

Among the ahadith describing the actions of the Prophet, may Allah bless him and grant him peace, it is said that he used to give sadaqa, one for each joint. It is also said in the ahadith describing his actions that he used to give sadaqa every day, one for each bone.

The Prophet, may Allah bless him and grant him peace, said, "If the lump of flesh in the placenta is at peace, then all of the placenta is at peace, and if it is corrupt, then all of the placenta is corrupt, except for one part – which is the heart."

It has been related by Abu Huraira that the Prophet, may Allah bless him and grant him peace, said, "The stomach is the storage container of the body, and the blood vessels are watered by it. If the stomach is healthy, the blood vessels remain healthy after being watered by it, but if the stomach is diseased, then the blood vessels end up becoming diseased as well." Abu Nu'aim has also quoted this hadith.

From Ibn 'Umar comes the hadith which states that the mumin fills one stomach when he eats, while the kafir fills seven stomachs when he eats.

Al-Bukhari and Muslim have transmitted the hadith which states that the stomach is an organ which is well-supplied with nerves and which is shaped like a hollow gourd, with a long neck. The opening at the upper end is called the oesophagus, through which food and drink are passed. The opening at the lower end is called the pylorus, through which the contents of the stomach are passed down into the intestines. The pylorus is also known as 'al-fu'ad'. The inside of the stomach is lined with villi, especially in the central area, and they are the seat of any disease which arises when this is the place where the first phase of digestion takes place. It is here that the food is processed and then passed on to the liver. The stomach has been supplied with nerves so that it can expand towards the liver. The other reason why it has been supplied with nerves is so that it can expand, when it is filled with food, without bursting.

Continuing on down from the stomach are the three small intestines. The first is called the duodenum, and its length is twelve fingers. The second is called the jejunum, because it is usually empty. And the third one, which is long, fibrous and thin, is called the small intestine.

After these three come the three large intestines. The first is called the caecum, which is wide and without any outlet on either side. It is in here that the faeces first begin to stink. The second is called the colon, and the third is called the rectum, which ends with the anus. These are the six bowels which, counting the stomach as well, make seven, as referred to by the Prophet, may Allah bless him and grant him peace.

Ibn Sina said, "Truly it is because of Allah the Almighty's concern for mankind that He made more than just one intestine, and with intricacy, so that the passage of food down from the stomach would take some time."

Now the stomach is the source of all disease. The Prophet, may Allah bless him and grant him peace, said, "The stomach is the abode of disease." And he also said, "…if the stomach is diseased, then the blood vessels end up becoming diseased as well," – an observation which I have already quoted.

You should realise that Allah has formed the bodies of all creatures out of many organs. He has made bones so that the body is supported, and He did not merely put one bone in the body, but rather He put many bones there, because of its need to make many different movements – for if the body only had one bone, it would be incapable of making a variety of movements.

All bones are covered by a substance known as periosteum.

The Glorious and Almighty One has created a prominence at one end of every bone, and at the other end, a hollow – which is shaped to fit the prominence of the next bone which joins it. In this way the form of His creation has been perfected, and movement made easy.

As well as this, the Glorious and Almighty One has put the brain in its place, to act as the source of sensation and movement. It is from here that the nerves grow and connect to every organ, there being nerves which govern sensation, and nerves which govern movement. Out of all these nerves, He has connected one special kind to the eyes. This is called the optic nerve, and thanks to it, there is sight. He has connected another special nerve to the ears, and thanks to it, there is hearing. He has connected another special one to the nostrils, and thanks to it, there is the sense of smell. And He has connected yet another special nerve to the tongue, and thanks to it, there is taste.

The Glorious and Almighty One has made movement of the limbs possible thanks to the organs which are known as muscles, and he has increased the strength of the attachment of the muscles to the bones thanks to organs which are called tendons.

Now, since the lower parts of the body are relatively far away from the brain, the Creator made an opening in the underneath of the skull bone, through which the spinal cord passes. This then passes down inside the vertebrae of the back, and makes sensation and movement possible in the lower part of the body.

The Glorious and Almighty One has emphasised the importance of the brain by surrounding it with the skull bone, and of the spinal cord by surrounding it with the vertebrae – just in the same way that He has emphasised the importance of the heart and the liver by providing the breast bone. All these organs are vital organs, so He has protected them with bones so that they are far less likely to be damaged in any way.

The Glorious and Almighty One has placed three inner centres within the brain. The first – at the front – is concerned with the imagination, the second – in the middle – with reflection, and the third – at the back – with recollection.

In a similar manner, Allah the Glorious and Almighty, has made the heart the centre of life, and the source from which inner energy flows. And just as there are nerves which branch out from the brain in order to give sensation and movement to the organs, so there are glistening white arteries which branch out from the heart in order to give the organs life itself. And since the heart is the source of all inner energy, and of warmth in general, as soon as it stops beating, all energy ends.

Allah the Glorious and Praiseworthy has made the mouth and nostrils the means by which breathing is possible. Inside the mouth, there are two passageways, one for air to pass into the lungs, and the other for food and drink to pass into the oesophagus and stomach. Allah has made the lungs in order to ventilate and fan the heart, so that its energy is not stifled.

As regards the mouth, it has two parts. One part is specialised and is concerned with the sense of smell. The other part is formed in such a way that the air within it is conveyed to the heart, even though the mouth may be shut tight, as when sleeping, and when eating and drinking. If the mouth was not formed in this way, the tongue would cause suffocation during sleeping, and so the mouth would have to be kept open all the time, and during eating and drinking, the airway would be blocked – which would mean that if any morsel of food or drink entered the airway, then suffocation would result.

Just as Allah has made the brain and the heart the sources of sensation and movement and life for the rest of the body, so He has made the liver the source of nourishment for all the other organs, by means of the non-pulsating blood vessels.

When a person eats some food, first the lips taste it, then the canine teeth break it up, then the molars crush it, and then the tongue rolls it up. After all this, it is passed down to the stomach. If it simply remained in the stomach, then it would collect there, and eventually block the pyloric exit below with a solid mass. So this is when it is processed, while it is still there. For this processing to take place, fluid is needed, and so it is in these circumstances that a person feels thirsty. Accordingly, the stomach may feel warm, as a result of the work it is doing, and because of the moisture inside it. Once the processing, with the help of the fluid, has been completed, the result looks like a thin gruel.

Between the liver and the stomach, there are vessels by means of which food is conveyed from the stomach to the liver. This is part of the meaning of the Prophet's words, may Allah bless him and grant him peace, "The stomach is the storage container of the body, and the blood vessels are watered by it." The liver sucks up most of the liquid food by means of these vessels, and then a second phase of processing takes place, until the food has been converted into blood. As soon as it has become blood, it flows to all the organs, in as great a quantity as is needed for their well being.

Whatever food is left behind in the stomach – and it is the most nutritious – is expelled down into the intestine. These remains are expelled further down so that what is left of the food can be sent by the liver to the heart – in order to refine it, and to the lungs – in order to make them more subtle, and to the brain – in order to keep it moist, and to the bones – in order to make them thick and dry.

And so finally, all that remains in the intestine are the waste products. Of these, a certain amount is expelled to the gall bladder – where it becomes known as yellow bile, and a certain amount passes to the spleen – where it becomes known as black bile. A certain amount of yellow bile is then expelled from the gall bladder to the intestines, where it assists in the excretion of faeces, while a certain amount of black bile passes from the spleen to the mouth of the stomach, where it provokes the desire for food.

The blood absorbs a certain amount of fluid, in order to make it subtle enough to pass through narrow veins, after which it returns and passes back to the liver, from which it is expelled once again, but this time to the kidneys and the urinary bladder, where it becomes urine. A little of this comes from the blood which nourishes the kidneys and the bladder.

The fact that the fluid passes as far as the extremities of the organs, and then returns, can be proved by seeing what happens to the fluid when it is dyed – for after women have been using henna externally, their urine takes on a reddish colouring, just as if they had dyed the urine itself with henna.

There are two large vessels connected to the liver. One of them passes from its concave surface, and is called the portal vein. This is connected to the stomach, and collects the fluid from within it which has been produced from the food, as we have already described. The second large vessel passes from its convex surface, and is called the caval vein. This one branches out all over the body. One of its branches goes to the back-bone, and is called 'al-watayn', or 'the sustainer of the heart', because of its connection to the heart. It feeds all of a person's organs. It is also called 'an-niyat'. Ibn 'Abbas said, referring to this vein, "If it is severed, its owner dies." And this is the meaning of the words of Allah the Almighty, '... **and then severed his life-artery ...**' (Qur'an: 69.46), meaning by that the vessel which is known as al-watayn, or the aorta.

Another branch goes out from it to the throat, and is called 'al-warid', or the life vein. And of this one, Allah the Almighty says:

> **We certainly created man,**
> **and We know what his self whispers to him,**
> **and We are nearer to him than his life vein.**

> **(Qur'an: 50.16)**

It is also known as the jugular vein. It is the vein which is cut when an animal is being sacrificed. Another branch passes from it to the right chamber of the heart, which is known as al-abhar, or the superior vena cava. It is also referred to as the vessel which begins in the head, but the name I gave first is more accurate.

The Prophet, may Allah bless him and grant him peace, referred to this blood vessel during the illness from which he died, when he said, "Now my jugular vein has been cut, because of what I ate when I ate at Khaybar." Al-Asma'i said, "Al-abhar is the blood vessel within the back which is connected to the heart. If this is cut, it is not possible to continue living." As for his reference to what he ate, may Allah bless him and grant him peace, this is a reference to the shoulder of sheep which he tasted, and which had been poisoned by the accursed jewess, Zaynab bint al-Harath, the sister of Marhab. The effects of this poison were felt by him every year after that, just as they were at the time.

The rest of al-warid continues on to the head, and is called 'an-nama', or 'the melody'. It is referred to in the oath, 'May Allah end his an-nama' – that is, his song, or his life.

Then there is another branch which spreads out to the hands and ends there. One of its branches is called the cephalic vein, which is used for blood letting in cases where the disease is in the head, and another of its branches is called the basilic vein. From these two branches runs another single branch, which is known as the median vein. This is the vein which the Prophet, may Allah bless him and grant him peace, cauterised for Sa'd ibn Mu'adh, after he had been wounded on the fore-arm. Another of its branches is called the radial vein, two of whose branches are known as 'al-kitfi' and 'al-asaylam'. These veins run to the hands.

Another branch runs to the thighs, and is called the sciatic vein. It has already been described in the course of the description of how to treat the disease known as sciatica. (See pages 29 and 151). It is also used for blood letting when a woman ceases to menstruate. This provokes a flow again. The rest of this vein continues down through the legs, where it is known as the saphenous vein. It is used for blood letting in diseases of the feet.

Cutting any of these smaller veins does not terminate any life except its own. Indeed, if a man has his hand or foot cut off, he can still go on living. However, even in this case, he will not stay alive unless the wound is cauterised – and that is why the Prophet, may Allah bless him and grant him peace, cauterised the median vein in Sa'd's case.

You should know that the waste products of the digestion which takes place in the stomach are the faeces, and that the waste products of the digestion which takes place in the liver are the urine and black and yellow bile. The waste products of the digestion which takes place in the other organs are sweat and dirt. Every organ has its own waste products. For example, the waste products of the digestion which takes place in the brain are mucus and saliva, while those from the eyes are the sordes. During the night, the salt in this sometimes becomes infected. The waste products of the digestion which takes place in the heart and in the bladder are the growth of hair. The shari'ah requires that these hairs be plucked as regards the arm-pits, and shaved as regards the pubes. The waste products of the digestion which takes place in the ears is ear-wax. Sometimes, during the night, worms breed in this wax.

And all praise belongs to the Merciful One, the Compassionate One – **Allah** – the Divine Creator and Designer.

Since a single individual is unable to reproduce himself by himself, Allah the Majestic has created reproductive organs so that the species can be perpetuated. These organs are the penis and testicles in a man, and the womb and breasts in a woman. Allah has placed two large recesses in the womb, situated on the right and on the left. A male is usually formed in the right recess, and a female in the left. When twins are conceived, a male and a female, then both recesses are occupied.

When semen reaches the womb, the womb holds tightly on to it. This is because it is strongly attracted towards seminal fluid. The Prophet, may Allah bless him and grant him peace, whose word can not be doubted, stated that there is an angel in the womb who cries out, "O Lord, grant just one drop of semen!" And so when some semen reaches the womb, the womb holds tightly on to it – and from then on, the woman no longer desires to have sexual intercourse. This is one of the signs of pregnancy – that the woman stops wanting sexual intercourse. This sign is found in all animals.

According to the physicians, the womb is a greedy creature. When a man's semen meets a woman's fluid, the two fluids intermingle and interact. This results in bubbles forming, caused by the heat of the interaction, just in the same way that bubbles are produced when a thick fluid is heated over a fire. These bubbles then coalesce, making one single bubble, which forms a relatively large sphere. It is inside this sphere that the vital force will enter, by the permission of Allah.

Having expanded in this way, the semen then begins to acquire solidity. This stage is known as 'the stage of the clot', or 'al-'alaqa'. It is at this point that the guardian angel of the womb cries out, "O Lord, a man!", or, "O Lord, a woman!"

The next stage in the development of the clot is the formation of the blood vessels, which are needed for the purposes of nutrition. This stage is called 'the stage of the lump of flesh', or 'al-madhagha'.

After this, Allah, the Creator of all beings – Allah, Whose Name is Blessed – Allah, Whose majesty is infinite and Whose sovereignty is absolute, breathes the soul into it, and then the angel of the womb is commanded to write what has been decreed for this individual, as regards his provision, his life span, the actions with which he will fill his days, and whether he will be fortunate or unfortunate, as has been described in the ahadith.

After this, there are three membranes which form and surround the foetus. One of these is called 'al-mashima', and it attaches itself to the navel of the foetus in order to convey its nourishment to it – for it is through the navel that the foetus receives its nourishment while it lies within the womb of its mother.

The second membrane absorbs the urine of the foetus, while the third membrane absorbs all the other waste products from the foetus – which are the equivalent of the sweat and dirt which is excreted by the skin of a fully formed person.

All these facts are implied and indicated in the words of Allah Himself, when He says:

> **... He has created you in the wombs of your mothers, creation after creation, in three layers of darkness ...**

> **(Qur'an: 39.6)**

The words 'creation after creation' refer to the drop, the clot, and the lump of flesh, while the words 'three layers of darkness' indicate the three membranes.

And when the period which Allah has decreed for the pregnancy comes to an end, the three membranes are ruptured and broken, at which point the woman experiences pain, and the pangs of birth, and a flow of blood. This blood is known as the blood of parturition.

You should know that a baby usually sits in its mother's belly facing towards the back of the mother. When it wants to come out, it somersaults the top of its body to the lower end. If it did not do this, the baby would cling to its mother's abdomen with both hands, and both it and its mother would die. It is because of the severe pain that a woman endures, that a mother who dies during child-birth is classed by the 'ulama' as being a martyr – as the words of the Prophet, may Allah bless him and grant him peace, have taught us.

And so the baby comes out into this world, this place of trouble and worry and mistakes and wrong actions. Being new, the baby has nothing to give – neither harm, nor life, nor death, nor rebirth. Being beloved, his father and mother adore him and prepare the best that they have for him, and the choicest and most refined food. The affection of both strangers and family are directed at him, and whoever sees him, welcomes him – so weak is he.

After some time, he comes to the end of his time in this world of affliction and trial, where he has either been immersed in pleasure or else plunged into misery, and then his final destination is either the Garden or the Fire of Hell – may Allah protect us from the latter by His Generosity and Compassion, and grant that we be saved from such great misfortune, and grant us the grace to complete the actions of our life with a good ending.

So reflect, O man, on your beginning, and on your end, and on the consequences of your actions – and I ask the Majestic One Who is Forgiving to grant you all the grace to save your selves and be accepted into His Mercy.

Those who are experienced in this subject say that when a woman is pregnant with a male baby, her complexion improves and her step is lighter. The foetal movement of a male baby is felt more on the right side, and when the foetus is a male, the right breast of its mother grows larger than the left. The pulse in the wrist is also stronger, and when the mother starts walking, she puts the right foot forward first. All these indications are the opposite if the foetus is female.

As regards the words of the Prophet, may Allah bless him and grant him peace, "Truly He has created all of mankind with 360 joints," I will now list these for you, insh'Allah:

Experts in anatomy state that there are 11 bones in the cranium, 6 in the eye sockets, 2 in the cheeks, and 4 in the nose. To these are added the central incisors, the lateral incisors, the canines, and the molars, all of which are in the upper jaw. The same number are to be found in the lower jaw, which is also called the chin. So as regards the teeth bones, there are 16 above and 16 below, which are called, as already described above, the central and lateral incisors, the canines, and the molars.

The bones which form the back are joined above to the head bones, at the back. There are usually 24 vertebrae, but sometimes 1 more, and sometimes 1 less. They are joined below to the sacrum, which is the bone about which the Prophet, may Allah bless him and grant him peace, said, "All that will remain of the Tribe of Adam will be the tail-bone." The sacrum is joined below to the coccyx, numbering 6 bones altogether, and these are, as it were, the foundation for the rest of the body.

The 2 iliac bones are joined to the sacrum laterally, and in each of these there is the acetabulum, in which the head of the femur fits. This completes the description of the bones which form the back.

The bones which are at the front are made up of 2 clavicles and 2 scapulae, excluding the bones which are in the neck. Then there are 2 large bones, called the humerus, followed by the 4 bones of the forearms.

There are 7 bones in the chest, which are called the broad bones of the sternum. There are 12 ribs on either side, which are convex, and joined to the vertebrae behind. This completes the description of the bones which are at the front.

As for the hands, there are the bones which form the two wrists, which are 16 in number. All the bones of the carpus, which form the hand, are popularly known as the wrist. They are called the cuneiform bones, while the bone which adjoins the thumb is called the trapezium, and the one which lies opposite the little finger, the unciform. There are also the 8 bones of the metacarpus, and 30 bones which form the fingers – 3 bones in each finger – which are known as phalanges. We have already quoted what the Prophet, may Allah bless him and grant him peace, said about these.

As for the bones which form the legs, there are the 2 ischial bones (the femurs) – one in each thigh, 2 bones in the knees, and 4 bones below the knees. Below these, each foot has an astragalus, an os calcis, and a navicular bone, which form the ankle and enable the foot to be moved about. In all there are 8 bones. There are 20 bones in the foot, and 28 bones in the toes – 3 bones in each toe, except for the big toe, which only has 2.

And that completes the list of all the bones in the body, as enumerated by the Prophet, may Allah bless him and grant him peace.

Now since the bones are not placed in any fixed position, their Creator has clothed them with fibrous tissues round their extremities, in order to strengthen them and bind them together, which are called tendons and ligaments. He has also created muscles with which to move the bones, and there are 529 of these in the human body. The muscles are formed out of flesh and nerves.

And then He has connected all of these with arteries, and veins and nerves, so that they can be given life, and sensation, and movement, and nourishment – as has already been described. And then He has clothed them all with flesh, and fat, and adipose tissue.

The Creator has used the flesh to protect the organs from being ruptured, and to keep them safe from the cold, and from being split apart and separated from one another. Flesh such as this is called fascia, and it can be found, for example, in the thighs and in the tongue. The fat is a source of heat – indeed it is the essence of body heat, for a fire does not burn without fuel. And finally, the adipose tissue is the tissue which strengthens the organs which convey nutrition, by covering them like a coat. It facilitates digestion, and is plentiful in the peritoneum and the bowels.

And when He had finished creating this, the Almighty covered it all in skin! He made some skin thin, like the skin of the face, which needs to look beautiful or handsome, and He made other skin thick, like the skin of the feet, which are needed for walking and coming into contact with rough surfaces.

And then the Almighty placed organs of sensation and touch in the skin, and brought the mouths of blood vessels right up to it, so that every part of the skin has sensation, and so that blood will flow from wherever it is pricked, and so that it is capable of absorbing nourishment.

And then He made different kinds of hair – and nails – grow from the skin. He created some hair for its beauty, or as a veil, like the hair that grows on the head, or the eyebrows, or the eyelashes – for while the hair of the head and eyebrows are an adornment, the hair of the eyelashes is to protect the eyes from anything getting into them, as well as to make them look beautiful. For whenever we see a bald man with his eyebrows and eyelashes shaved off, that man is most certainly unpleasant to look at. Indeed, the ugliest aspect of a shaven monk is the ugliness of his face and its unpleasant appearance.

Among the acts of wisdom and mercy of the Praiseworthy and Almighty One, is the fact that He has made the hair of the eyebrows and eyelashes hardly grow at all – for if they were to grow long, they would cover the eyes and harm the eyesight, and if they grew straight up or straight down, they would make it difficult to see. Indeed, one of the diseases of the eyes is called trichiasis, or ingrowing eyelashes. This does considerable harm to the eyesight, and is remedied by plucking out the hair.

Another type of hair which is an adornment is the hair which grows from the chin, and which helps to give a man respect and dignity. Have you ever noticed how ugly eunuchs' faces are when they reach manhood?

Another type of hair, which is neither an adornment nor of any use, is the pubic hair and the hair under the armpits – and accordingly our Mighty Guide has commanded us to remove it and shave it off. And shaving off the pubic hair strengthens desire for sexual intercourse, just as shaving the back of the head strengthens the neck. There is nothing but mercy and blessing to be found in His creation.

And at the ends of the fingers He has created nails, which give added strength to their movements, and stop the tips of the fingers from being worn away. These have been made to grow steadily all the time, for if they were fixed and did not keep on growing, then they would be worn away as a result of all the work they have to do.

It is the sunnah to keep the nails trimmed – and the need to trim the nails and bury the trimmings are recorded in the ahadith, such as the hadith of the Prophet, may Allah bless him and grant him peace, "Keep the nails trimmed, and shave the pubic hair, and pluck the hair from the armpits, on Thursdays – and on Fridays, wear perfume, and clean clothes, and have a ghusl." As regards having a ghusl on Fridays, this is sometimes necessary and sometimes only desirable.

It is stated in the ahadith that whoever cuts his nails will not suffer from ophthalmia on the other side.

It is also stated in the ahadith that hair and nail trimmings should be buried, in case the Tribe of Adam use them for the purposes of magic. According to one hadith, which has a strong isnad, it has been related by Mujahid, "Burying nail trimmings is desirable," and the same isnad adds, " and it is also desirable to bury blood and hair." It has been related that Abu Daw'ud once said, "Once the Prophet, may Allah bless him and grant him peace, was cupped, and afterwards he said to the man, 'Bury the blood, in case it is licked by a dog suffering from rabies.'"

So may the blessings of Allah and His peace be on this illiterate Prophet, who so marvellously transmitted the knowledge that helps us to perceive and which dazzles those who are wise, and who has given us understanding of His everlasting gifts which continue to unfold by day and by night. In doing this, Allah the Praiseworthy and Almighty has made man glad through His Excellence and Mercy – and may His slaves worship him with deep understanding, and praise be to Allah, the Lord of the worlds.

Listening to Recitation

Listening to recitation is the perfume of the souls, the calmer of hearts, and the food of the spirit. It is one of the most important psychological medicines. It is a source of pleasure, even to some animals – and pleasure in moderation purifies inner energy, enhances the functioning of the faculties, slows down senile decay by driving out its diseases, improves the complexion, and refreshes the entire body. Pleasure in excess, on the other hand, makes the illnesses of the body grow worse.

Abu Nu'aim states, in his *Tibb an-Nabbi*, that the Prophet, may Allah bless him and grant him peace, said that the benefits of listening to recitation are increased when it is understood – that is, when its meaning is understood. Allah Himself says:

> ... so give good news to My slaves,
> those who listen to the Word
> and then follow the best of it ...

(Qur'an: 39.17-18)

Abu Huraira said, "Fortunate are the ones whom Allah has allowed – amongst the things that He has allowed His slaves – to recite the Qur'an, or to raise their voices in sweet songs, or even just to listen to them, and to recite or sing with sweet cadences."

The Prophet, may Allah bless him and grant him peace, said, "They adorned the Qur'an with their voices." And again, there are also these words of Allah:

> ... He increases whatever He wants in the creation ...

(Qur'an: 35.1)

This can include 'by means of a beautiful voice'.

Dhu'n-Nun was once asked, "What is meant by 'recitation'?" And he replied, "It is what conveys the truth and what points hearts towards the Truth." When he was asked to define what a beautiful voice is, he replied, "It is speech and intonation to which Allah the Almighty has added perfume."

It has been related that one day 'Umar ibn al-Khattab, may Allah be pleased with him, was reciting in his house, and someone made a remark about it, to which he replied, "Even if I am alone, I recite, as men are accustomed to do." And then he added, "Recitation is the provision of travellers!"

'Abdullah ibn Ja'far was extremely fond of recitation.

One day az-Zuhri was asked whether he disliked songs, to which he replied, "Yes, if they are not pleasing – for example if they are very dull or very frivolous."

The Prophet Daw'ud, peace be on him, had a very sweet voice, even when lamenting his wrong actions. Whenever he recited the Zabur, everyone used to gather round him – people, jinn, birds and wild animals. Once the Prophet, may Allah bless him and grant him peace, commented on a song to Abu Musa, saying, "Truly, I would describe this song as one of the songs that has been inherited from Daw'ud."

Plato said that there are only four pleasures in this world: eating, drinking, making love and listening to singing. Indeed, you can observe that most people whose work is physically tiring – such as dyers and porters, for example – make up tunes for themselves, by means of which they ease their weariness. You also see how crying babies are quietened by a lullaby. And camels are encouraged to cover long distances through singing to them.

There is a story that there was once a certain Arab who had a slave who had a very sweet voice, and whenever he had a camel that was very heavily laden, he used to sing to it. One camel like this once completed a three day journey in a single day, and after arriving, she lay down and died. If a camel can be so affected by a sweet voice, when it does not even understand the meaning of the words, what then will be the effect on people who have good taste and are well educated when they not only hear an exquisite voice, but also understand the beauty of the words as well?

Perhaps you have observed how nightingales and the birds called ash-shuhrur seek out places for themselves where they can listen to their singing.

As regards whether or not it is halal to listen to songs, some 'ulama' say that this pleasure is permitted, and others that it is not. According to Ibn Qataba, songs and harmonious recitation clear the mind, sweeten the self, bring life to the soul, purify the blood, improve and help the condition of people with thick diseases, and develop all the natural qualities in a person. Listening to singing is recommended as part of the treatment for some diseases, especially those which are due to the spleen.

Small Pox, Measles and Chicken Pox

Small Pox

You should know that there are several varieties of small pox, including white, yellow, violet, green and black pox. The least dangerous is white small pox – for when the pus is white and the sediment in the urine is white, this indicates that the constitution is still relatively strong, which is not the case with the red, yellow, violet and green types. Black small pox is the most dangerous.

If there are only a few spots, or if the spots are large, this means that there is less danger, for these indicate that the diseased matter is not powerful and that the constitution is relatively strong. An exception to this is when the spots are 'doubled' – that is, when one variety appears on top of another one. If there are many spots, or if the spots are small, these are bad signs. The safest type is when the eruption begins on or about the third day after the rash first appears. If a rash is slow to erupt, this is a bad sign, for it indicates that the diseased matter is powerful, and the constitution relatively weak.

When the rash appears once, and then erupts a second time, it should be feared. When there is a free flow of the illness, this indicates safety – and vice versa. When the pustules look elongated, the danger is greater, and when they look round, it is less dangerous. If the rash appears on the chest and the abdomen, this is most dangerous, for it indicates that the diseased matter is too strong to be expelled to the extremities of the body. The type that appears on the extremities is not as bad as the one which appears on the face and head. The type which is accompanied by a fever and restlessness is safer – and vice versa. When the fever precedes the rash, this is less dangerous than when the rash precedes the fever. When the respiration is good, this indicates safety, and when respiration is difficult, then there is danger. When there is shortness of breath accompanied by thirst, then you should realise that one of the fatal types of the pox is present. And when the urine is bloody or black, then the outcome is always death.

Measles

Measles, like small pox, arises from bitter bile. The diseased matter is in the blood.

Chicken Pox

Chicken pox lies mid-way between small pox and measles.

When treating it, it is essential to provoke a good flow, and to expel the disease from the blood by using blood letting and scarification. The patient should drink grape and pomegranate syrup, and eat peas and spinach, and a milk pudding made with almonds and barley water, mixed with almond oil. Eye drops made with coriander water, and into which black collyrium has been sprinkled, should be administered, and the soles of the feet should be dyed with henna.

When the fever abates, the patient should have some soup made from young chickens – and after 20 days, he should have a hot bath.

And Allah Knows everything.

And so this book is finished with praise and help from Allah
– and may whoever relies on Him be blessed!

Glossary of Arabic Terms

Adam : the first man, created from clay, peace be on him.

ahadith : plural of hadith.

akhira : the next world, what is on the other side of death, the world after this world in the realm of the Unseen.

'alim : a man of knowledge from amongst the Muslims who acts on what he knows.

Allah – ta'ala : Allah – the Most High, the Lord of all the worlds. Allah, the supreme and mighty Name, indicates the One, the Existent, the Creator, the Worshipped, the Lord of the Universe. Allah is the First without beginning and the Last without end and the Outwardly Manifest and the Inwardly Hidden.

amir : one who commands, the source of authority in any given situation.

Ansar : the 'Helpers', the people of Madina who welcomed and aided the Messenger of Allah, may Allah bless him and grant him peace, when he made hijrah to Madina.

awliya : plural of wali.

ayah : a sign, a verse of the Qur'an.

ayat : plural of ayah.

bani Adam : the tribe of Adam, mankind in a genetic sense.

baraka : a blessing, any good which is bestowed by Allah, and especially that which increases; a subtle beneficent spiritual energy which can flow through things and people or places. It is experienced in certain places more strongly than in others, and in some places and objects overpoweringly so. Its highest realm of activity is the human being. Purity permits its flow, for it is purity itself, which is Light. Density of perception blocks it. It is transformative, healing and immeasurable.

Bismillahi'r-Rahmani'r-Rahim : 'In the Name of Allah the Merciful the Compassionate'.

daniq : a small weight based on the weight of an ancient coin bearing the same name, weighing approximately 0.50 gms.

Da'wud : the Prophet David, peace be on him.

deen : the life-transaction, submission and obedience to a particular system of rules and practices; a debt of exchange between two parties, in this usage between the Creator and the created. Allah says in the Qur'an, **'Surely the deen with Allah is Islam.'** (Qur'an: 3.19).

dinar : a gold coin weighing approximately 4.40 gms.

dirham : a silver coin weighing approximately 3.08 gms.

dhimmi : a non-Muslim living under the protection of Muslim rule.

drachm : a small weight based on the weight of an ancient Greek coin bearing the same name, weighing approximately 3.5 gms.

du'a : making supplication to Allah.

dunya : the world, not as cosmic phenomenon but as it is experienced; this world as opposed to the akhira.

faqih: an 'alim with a sound knowledge of the shari'ah, who by virtue of his knowledge is able to make a legal judgement.

fard : obligatory, an obligatory act of worship or practice of the deen, as defined by the shari'ah.

fatwa : an authoritative legal opinion or judgement given by a faqih.

ghusl : the full ritual washing of the body with water alone to be pure for the prayer.

hadith : reported speech, particularly of, or about, the Prophet Muhammad, may Allah bless him and grant him peace.

hadith qudsi : those words of Allah on the tongue of His Prophet, may Allah bless him and grant him peace, which are not part of the Revelation of the Qur'an.

hajj : the yearly pilgrimage to Makka which every Muslim who has the means and ability must make once in his or her life-time, and the performance of the rites of the Hajj in the protected area which surrounds the Ka'aba.

hakim : a wise man, particularly a doctor.

halal : permitted by the shari'ah.

haram : forbidden by the shari'ah; also a protected area, an inviolable place or object.

Haram : a protected area in which certain behaviour is forbidden and other behaviour necessary. The area around the Ka'aba in Makka is a Haram, and the area around the Prophet's Mosque, in which is the Prophet Muhammad's tomb, may Allah bless him and grant him peace, in Madina, is a Haram. They are referred to together as the Haramayn.

harisa : either a savoury meat and wheat dish, or a sweet pastry made with flour, melted butter and sugar.

Hawwa : Eve, the first woman, the partner of Adam, peace be on them.

Hijaz : the region along the western seaboard of Arabia, in which Makka, Madina, Jeddah and Ta'if are situated.

hijrah : emigration in the way of Allah. Islam takes its dating from the Hijrah of the Prophet Muhammad, may Allah bless him and grant him peace, from Makka to Madina, in 622 CE.

hikma : wisdom.

Ibrahim : the Prophet Abraham, peace be on him.

ihram : the conditions of clothing and behaviour adopted by someone on Hajj or Umrah.

ihsan : the state of being absolutely sincere to Allah in oneself; it is to worship Allah as though you see Him, knowing that although you do not see Him, He sees you.

imam : the one who leads the prayer, an eminent scholar.

iman : acceptance, belief, trust, in Allah. Iman is to believe in Allah, His angels, His revealed books, His messengers, the Last Day and the Garden and the Fire, and that everything is by the Decree of Allah, both the good of it and the bad of it.

Injil : the original Gospel which was revealed to the Prophet Jesus, peace be on him.

insh'Allah : 'if Allah wills it', 'God willing'.

Isa : the Prophet Jesus, peace be on him.

Islam : peace and submission to the will of Allah, the way of life embodied by all the prophets, given its final form in the prophetic guidance brought by the Prophet Muhammad, may the blessings and peace of Allah be on him. The five pillars of Islam are the affirmation of the shahada, doing the salat, paying the zakat, fasting the month of Ramadan, and doing the hajj once in your lifetime if you are able.

isnad : the record, either memorised or recorded in writing, of the names of the people who form the chain of human transmission, person to person, by means of which a hadith is preserved – and accordingly these people themselves. One of the sciences of the Muslims which was developed after the Prophet Muhammad's death, may Allah bless him and grant him peace, is the science of assessing the authenticity of a hadith by assessing the reliability of its isnad.

Jahannam : a name for Hell.

jahiliyya : the time of ignorance, before the coming of Islam.

Jahim : the fire of Hell.

janaba : the impure state in which a person requires a ghusl before prayer is permissible again.

jannah : the Garden, Paradise, the final destination and resting place of the muminun in the akhira once the Last Day is over.

Jibril : the archangel Gabriel who brought the Revelation of the Qur'an to the Prophet Muhammad, may the blessings and peace of Allah be on him.

jinn : unseen beings created from smokeless fire who co-habit the earth together with mankind.

jumu'a : the day of gathering, Friday, and particularly the jumua prayer which is prayed instead of the mid-day prayer by all those who are present at the mosque to do the prayer.

junub : being in the state of janaba.

Ka'aba : the cube-shaped building at the centre of the Haram in Makka, originally built by the Prophet Ibrahim, peace be on him, and rebuilt with the help of the Prophet Muhammad, may Allah bless him and grant him peace; also known as the House of Allah. The Ka'aba is the focal point which all Muslims face when doing the salat. This does not mean that Allah lives inside the Ka'aba, nor does it mean that the Muslims worship the Ka'aba. It is Allah Who is worshipped and Allah is not contained or confined in any form or place or time or concept.

kafir : a person who commits kufr, an unbeliever, one who covers up the true nature of existence, the opposite of a mumin.

kafirun : the plural of kafir.

kohl : antimony powder used both as a decoration and as a medicine for the eyes.

kufr : to cover up the truth, to reject Allah and His Messenger, may the blessings and peace of Allah be on him.

la ilaha illa'llah : there is no god except Allah.

madhdhab : a school of fiqh, particularly those deriving from the four great scholars of Islam: Imam Malik, Imam Abu Hanifa, Imam Shafi'i, and Imam Ibn Hanbal.

Madina : the City, often called Madina al-Munawarra – the illuminated, or the enlightened, city – where the revelation of the Qur'an was completed and in which the Prophet Muhammad died and is buried, may Allah bless him and grant him peace.

Makka : the city in which the Ka'aba stands, and in which the Prophet Muhammad was born, may Allah bless him and grant him peace, and where the revelation of the Qur'an commenced.

makruh : disapproved of without being forbidden, by the shari'ah.

mala'ika : the angels, who are made of light and glorify Allah unceasingly. They are neither male nor female. They do not need food or drink. They are incapable of wrong action and disobedience to Allah. They do whatever Allah commands them to do.

Maryam : Mary, the mother of Jesus, peace be on her and him; the only woman to be mentioned by name in the Qur'an.

ma sha'Allah : 'what Allah wants' happens.

Mika'il : the archangel Michael.

mimbar : steps on which the Imam stands to deliver his speech on the day of the jumua.

mithqal : a small unit of weight, approximately 4.50 gms.

muhadithun : people who transmit and study hadith.

Muhajirun : Companions of the Messenger of Allah, may Allah bless him and grant him peace, who accepted Islam in Makka and made hijrah to Madina.

Muhammad ar-Rasulu'llah : Muhammad is the Messenger of Allah, may the blessings and peace of Allah be on him.

Muharram : the first month of the Muslim year, which is based on the lunar calendar, and one of the four inviolable months during which fighting is prohibited – haram – from which its name is derived.

muhsin : someone who possesses the quality of ihsan.

mumin : a believer, someone who possesses the quality of iman, who trusts in Allah and accepts His Messenger, may Allah bless him and grant him peace.

muminun : the plural of mumin.

munafiq : a hypocrite; the hypocrites outwardly profess Islam on the tongue, but inwardly reject Allah and His Messenger, may Allah bless him and grant him peace, siding with the kafirun against the Muslims. The deepest part of the Fire is reserved for them.

munafiqun : the plural of munafiq.

Musa : the Prophet Moses, peace be on him.

mushrik : one who commits shirk.

mushrikun : the plural of mushrik.

muslim : someone who follows the way of Islam, doing what is obligatory, avoiding what is forbidden, keeping within the limits prescribed by Allah, and following the sunnah of the Prophet Muhammad, may Allah bless him and grant him peace, in what he or she is able. A Muslim is, by definition, one who is safe and sound, at peace in this world, and promised the Garden in the next world.

muslimun : the plural of muslim.

mustahab : what is recommended, but not obligatory, in acts of worship in the shari'ah.

nabidh : a drink made by soaking grapes, raisins, dates and so on in water without their being allowed to ferment.

Nar : the Fire of Jahannam, Hell, the final destination and place of torment of the kafirun and munafiqun in the akhira once the Last Day is over.

Nuh : the Prophet Noah, peace be on him.

qintar : a relatively large measure of weight, approximately 45 kgs.

qirat : a measure of weight with contrary meanings, either a very small weight of approximately 0.25 gms, or a very great weight like that of a mountain!

Qur'an : the 'Recitation', the last revelation from Allah to mankind and the jinn before the end of the world, revealed to the Prophet Muhammad, may Allah bless him and grant him peace, through the angel Jibril, over a period of twenty-three years, the first thirteen of which were spent in Makka and the last ten of which were spent in Madina. The Qur'an amends, encompasses, expands, surpasses and abrogates all the earlier revelations revealed to the earlier messengers, peace be on all of them. The Messenger of Allah said, may Allah bless him and grant him peace, that each verse of the Qur'an has an outward meaning and an inward meaning and a gnostic meaning. The Qur'an is the greatest miracle given to the Prophet Muhammad by Allah, for he was illiterate and could neither read nor write. The Qur'an is the uncreated word of Allah. The Qur'an still exists today exactly as it was originally revealed, without any alteration or change or addition or deletion. Whoever recites the Qur'an with courtesy and sincerity receives knowledge and wisdom, for it is the well of wisdom in this age.

Rafa'il : the archangel Raphael, whose name means 'the one who heals'.

rak'a : a unit of the prayer, a complete series of standing, bowing, prostrations and sittings.

rak'at : the plural of rak'a.

Ramadan : the month of fasting, the ninth month in the Muslim lunar calendar, during which all adult Muslims who are in good health fast from the first light of dawn until sunset each day. The Qur'an was first revealed in the month of Ramadan.

ruh : the spirit which gives life, formed from pure light; also the angel Jibril.

ruqya : recitation of verses of the Qur'an for treatment of, and protection against, illness.

sadaqa : giving in the way of Allah, a gift to another or others without any other motive than the giving.

sahih : healthy and sound with no defects; often used to describe a fully authenticated hadith. The two most reliable collections of hadith by al-Bukhari and Muslim are both called Sahih.

sajda : the act of making prostration, particularly in the prayer.

salat : the prayer, particularly the five daily obligatory ritual prayers of the Muslims which are called maghrib, 'isha, fajr, dhur and 'asr. They consist of fixed numbers of rak'at in worship to Allah.

salih : a spiritually developed man. By definition, one who is in the right place at the right time.

salihun : the plural of salih.

salla'llahu alayhi wa sallam : 'may Allah bless him and grant him peace', meaning the Prophet Muhammad.

sawm : fasting, particularly the fast of Ramadan, from food and drink – and making love if you are married – during daylight, from the first light of dawn until sunset.

shahada : to witness, to bear witness that there is no god except Allah and that Muhammad is the Messenger of Allah, may Allah bless him and grant him peace.

shahid : a witness, a martyr in the way of Allah.

Sham : the territory north of Arabia which is now divided into Syria, Palestine, Lebanon and Jordan.

shari'ah : a road, the legal and social modality of a people based on the revelation of their Prophet. The last shari'ah in history is that of Islam. It abrogates all previous shari'ahs. It is, being the last, the easiest to follow, for it is applicable to the whole human race wherever they are.

shaykh : an old man, an 'alim who has knowledge of Allah and of His Messenger, may Allah bless him and grant him peace, and of the deen of Islam; the one who guides you from knowledge of your self to knowledge of your Lord.

shayatin : the plural of shaytan.

shaytan : a devil, particularly Iblis (Satan), an evil jinn who prompts mankind and the jinn to rebel against Allah. Shaytan is part of the creation of Allah, and we seek refuge in the perfect word of Allah from the evil that He has created.

shirk : the unforgivable wrong action of worshipping something or someone other than Allah or associating something or someone as a partner with Him; the opposite of Tawhid which is affirmation of Divine Unity. Shirk is idol-worship, which is attributing form to Allah by attempting to confine Him within an object, a concept, a ritual or a myth – whereas Allah is not like anything and has no form. He cannot be conceived of or perceived.

shuhada : plural of shahid.

siddiq : a man of truth. Sincerity is his condition, not his adopted position.

Siffin : a place in Syria where in 36 AH, a battle between forces loyal to the amir al-muminin 'Ali ibn Abi Talib, may Allah be pleased with him, and forces supporting the claims of Mu'awiyya ibn Abi Sufyan took place.

Sulayman : The Prophet Solomon, peace be on him.

sunnah : a form, the customary practice of a person or group of people. It has come to refer almost exclusively to the practice of the Messenger of Allah, Muhammad, may Allah bless him and grant him peace, but also comprises the customs of the first generation of Muslims in Madina, who acted in accordance with what they had learned from him and who transmitted what they had learned to the next generation. The sunnah is a complete behavioural science that has been systematically kept outside the learning framework of this society, but which nevertheless has been preserved by those to whom it has been transmitted and who continue to embody it as their way of life. The Messenger of Allah, may Allah bless him and grant him peace, said, "My sunnah is my medicine."

surah : a form, a large unit of the Qur'an, composed of ayat linked by thematic content.

Surat'al-Fatiha : the opening surah of the Qur'an, the surah of both Opening and Victory:

Bismillahi'r-Rahmani'r-Rahim

**Al-hamduli'llahi rabbi'l-alameen,
Ar-Rahmani'r-Rahim,
Maliki yawmi'd-deen.
Iyyaka na'budu wa iyyaka nasta'een.
Ihdina's-sirat al-mustaqim,
sirat alladheen an'amta alayhim
ghayri'l-maghdhubi alayhim wa la'dh-dhalleen.**

Amin

Which means:

In the Name of Allah the Merciful the Compassionate

Praise to Allah, Lord of the Worlds,
the Merciful the Compassionate,
King of the Day of the Life-Transaction.
Only You we worship and only You we ask for help.
Lead us on the Straight Path,
The path of those whom You have blessed,
Not of those with whom You are angry,
and not of those who are astray.

Amen

(Qur'an: 1.1-7)

Surat'al-Ikhlas : the surah of Sincerity:

Bismillahi'r-Rahmani'r-Rahim

Qul Huwa'llahu Ahad
Allahu's-Samad
Lam yalid wa lam yuwlad
Wa lam yakun lahu kufuwan Ahad.

Which means:

In the Name of Allah the Merciful the Compassionate

Say: He is Allah the One
Allah the Everlasting
No one is born from Him and He is not born from anything
And there is nothing like Him.

(Qur'an: 112.1-4)

tabaraka'llah : Blessed is Allah.

talabina : barley soup.

taqwa : being careful, knowing your place in the cosmos. Its proof is the experience of awe, of Allah, which inspires a person to be on guard against wrong action and eager for actions which please Him.

tarawih : extra night prayers in the month of fasting, Ramadan, in order to recite the Qur'an as fully as possible, or completely.

Tawhid : the Divine Unity, Unity in its most profound sense. Allah is One in His Essence and His Attributes and His Acts.

Tawrah : the Torah which was revealed to the Prophet Moses, peace be on him.

tharid : meat and vegetable broth.

'ulama' : the plural of alim.

Umm al-Muminin : 'Mother of the Believers', an honorary title given to the wives of the Prophet, may the blessings and peace of Allah be on him and on his family.

Umm al-Qur'an : 'Mother of the Qur'an', the opening surah of the Qur'an which is called Al-Fatiha; also said to be its source in the Unseen.

umrah : the lesser pilgrimage to the Ka'aba in Makka and the performance of its rites in the protected area which surrounds the Ka'aba. You can do Umrah at any time of the year.

wajib : a necessary part of the shari'ah but not obligatory.

wali : a guardian, a person who has responsibility for another person; used particularly for the person who 'gives' a woman in marriage. Also someone who is a 'friend' of Allah, a person who has intimate knowledge of Allah.

wudu : ritual washing of the hands, mouth, nostrils, face, forearms, head, ears and feet with water alone so as to be pure for the prayer. You must already be in ghusl for wudu to be effective.

Zabur : the Psalms which were revealed to the Prophet David, peace be on him.

Zamzam : the well in the Haram of Makka which has the best water in the world!

Glossary of Medical Terms

abluent : an agent which cleanses and purifies.

amnesia : partial or total loss of memory.

aperient : a mild laxative.

apoplexy : sudden loss of muscular control, with diminution or loss of sensation and consciousness, resulting from rupture or blocking of a blood vessel in the brain; a stroke.

astringent : tending to draw together or constrict tissue.

belleric : brown myrobalan, principally from Afghanistan.

branding : a form of cauterisation, using branding irons.

carminative : inducing the expulsion of gas from the stomach and intestines.

cauterisation : to burn or sear with a cautery.

cautery : a very hot branding iron, used to destroy diseased or abnormal tissue, or to seal a vein or artery which is bleeding too profusely for the blood to be able to clot by itself.

chebulic : black myrobalan, principally from India.

chloasma : brown patches on the skin, usually on the face, which can occur during pregnancy or the menopause.

coctant : a digesting agent, anything which aids the digestion.

coction : the process of digestion, or of interaction, or of boiling.

confection : a medicine that has been sweetened.

cordial : a sweet, fruit-based, non-alcoholic drink, often used when treating the heart.

decoctant : a digesting agent, anything which aids the digestion.

decoction : the resulting liquid when a substance or herb has been concentrated by being boiled in water.

detergent : a cleansing agent.

diarrhoea : excessive and frequent evacuation of watery faeces.

diuretic : an agent which increases the production and discharge of urine.

dropsy : excessive accumulation of fluid in the body tissues and cavities.

ebullient : an agent which causes heat and movement.

electuary : a medicine mixed with sugar and water or with honey, and made into a paste or syrup.

embrocation : a lotion or ointment for rubbing on the skin.

emetic : an agent which causes vomiting.

emmenagogue : an agent which precipitates or stimulates menstruation.

emollient : an agent which soothes or softens, especially the skin.

enema : liquid injected into the rectum, for laxative, cleansing, or other therapeutic purposes.

enuresis : involuntary urination.

erysipelas : an acute fiery skin infection, marked by spreading inflammation, particularly on the face and scalp.

haemorrhage : bleeding, from a ruptured blood vessel, either externally or internally.

haemostatic : an agent which stops or prevents bleeding.

hemicrania : a headache affecting only one side of the head, usually a migraine.

herpes : a creeping skin infection causing eruptions on the skin or mucous membrane.

infusion : the resulting liquid when a substance or herb has been left to soak in water which has just been boiled.

laxative : an agent that relaxes and stimulates evacuation of the bowels.

lenitive : an agent that eases pain or discomfort.

leucoderma : partial or total lack of skin pigmentation, resulting in white patches; also called vitiligo.

linctus : a liquid, syrupy medicine taken to relieve coughs.

oedema : excessive accumulation of fluid in the body tissues and cavities; also called dropsy.

oxymel : a syrup whose main ingredients are honey and vinegar.

palsy : paralysis, muscle weakness marked by loss of power to feel or control movement in any part of the body.

paracentesis : tapping, puncturing the skin in order to draw off excess fluid from a part of the body, often through a hollow needle.

paraesthesia : an abnormal sensation of prickling, tingling, or itching of the skin, caused by disorder in the nerves.

pessary : a vaginal suppository, usually used either as a form of contraception, or as a means of facilitating pregnancy; also a form of support inserted in the vagina to prevent a prolapse of the uterus.

phthisis : tuberculosis; also wasting away and emaciation of part or all of the body.

pleurisy : inflammation of the membranes which cover both the lungs and the inner surface of the chest wall, characterised by pain in the chest or side which becomes worse when breathing deeply or coughing.

purgative : a cleaning and clearing out agent, a laxative.

purge : another word for purgative.

resolvent : an agent which reduces inflammation and swelling; also an agent which causes a substance to break down and separate into its constituents.

solvent : a loosener, a laxative; also a liquid which is capable of dissolving another substance.

stomatitis : inflammation of the mucous lining of the mouth, sometimes with ulcers.

subtilant : a diluting agent.

suppository : a solid medication designed to melt within a body cavity other than the mouth, especially the rectum or vagina. Rectal suppositories are used in the treatment of piles and to ease constipation and facilitate defecation. Vaginal suppositories are usually used either as a form of contraception, or as a means of facilitating pregnancy; also known as pessaries.

tenesmus : a painful attempt to urinate or defecate; also the uncontrollable painful spasms which occur when there are frequent attempts to defecate, with hardly anything being produced.

tisane : a herbal infusion or similar preparation, drunk either as a beverage, or for its mildly medicinal effect.

urticaria : a skin condition characterised by intensely itching red, raised patches or weals, usually caused by an allergic reaction to internal or external agents.

vertigo : dizziness, the feeling that either one's self or surroundings are tilting or whirling around.

vitiligo : partial or total lack of skin pigmentation, resulting in white patches; also called leucoderma.

Index

B

M

ma' 100.
madhagha 194.
Madina 207, 209.
madness 17, 20, 106, 133, 166.
maghafir 103.
magic 108, 130, 167, 170, 198. *See also* incantations; spells.
magnets 88.
mahmuda 102.
main organs 146, 147.
making love 200, 211.
Makka 70, 207, 209.
makruh 176, 208.
ma'l-ward 102.
mala'ika 208.
male 185, 193, 195, 208.
mallows 57, 118, 150, 151.
man 77, 88, 122, 184, 186, 191, 193.
manhood 163, 198.
manias 20.
mankind 78, 111, 131, 144, 188, 195, 207, 209, 211.
manna 69, 90, 103, 117.
marjan 102.
marjoram 102.
marriage 18, 136, 214.
marrows 129.
marsh mallows 59, 151.
martyrs 46, 159, 160, 161, 162, 177, 194, 211.
Mary 45, 208.
marzanjush 102.
mash 102.
mashima 194.
massalah milah 104.
mastaki 103.

mastic 103, 118, 150, 151.
masturbation 21.
matting 40, 86.
maturity 186.
meaning 210.
means of livelihood 185.
measles 82, 202.
meat 10, 20, 36, 37, 39, 40, 41, 57, 74, 80, 89, 96, 97, 98, 104, 147, 149, 151.
  beasts of prey 98.
  beef 98, 151.
  birds 98.
  birds of prey 98.
  camel 96, 98, 151.
  chicken 61, 69, 147.
  crow 83.
  domestic ass 98.
  doves 55.
  frog 75, 144.
  gazelle 83.
  goat 74, 97, 98.
  hoopoe 108.
  horse 98.
  kid's 147, 148, 156.
  lamb's 57, 147.
  lizard 74.
  mutton 74, 97.
  quail 69.
  rabbit 37.
  snake 143.
  sparrow 81.
  spleen 75.
  veal 98.
  wild ass 98.
medicine 18, 21, 22, 26, 29, 30, 33, 34, 40, 49, 50, 52, 53, 62, 67, 69, 70, 75, 77, 78, 79, 80, 81, 85, 86, 87, 95, 103, 105, 111, 113, 118, 121, 122, 123, 124, 125, 126, 127, 129,

W

waja' 172.
walking 186, 195, 197.
walnuts 47, 49.
waras 109.
ward 109.
warid 191, 192.
warts 50.
washing 140, 145, 172, 204.
washing the dead 67, 136.
washma 110.
wasps 61.
waste products 16, 173, 190, 192, 193, 194.
wasting away 48, 96, 152, 217.
watayn 191.
water 14, 15, 16, 24, 29, 33, 40, 41, 44, 46, 47, 63, 64, 65, 78, 79, 80, 92, 93, 94, 100, 101, 103, 104, 105, 109, 113, 117, 130, 135, 138, 140, 144, 145, 147, 148, 149, 150, 151, 152, 155, 156, 157, 161, 165, 167, 169, 170, 172, 181, 204, 209, 214, 215, 216.
water lilies 107.
water lily blossom 117.
water melons 123.
water-skins 10, 15, 100, 101, 145.
wax 111, 193.
  bees' 62.
way of Allah 162.
weakness 43, 147, 155, 161.
wealth 11.
weaning 186.
weariness 200.

weeping 182, 183.
wet dreams 10, 42.
wheat 36, 55, 71, 105, 137.
wheat bran 105.
whisperings 171.
wild asses 55.
wild thyme 107.
wind 10, 35, 38, 39, 43, 47, 50, 51, 54, 55, 58, 63, 66, 71, 73, 78, 84, 87, 90, 91, 93, 102, 103, 148, 150.
wind-pipe 86.
wine 53, 54, 59, 88, 99, 141, 142, 143, 151.
winter 9, 23, 26, 80, 108, 130.
wisdom 13, 15, 17, 22, 26, 40, 112, 113, 176, 177, 197, 210.
withdrawal 164.
witnesses 136.
womb 185, 193, 194.
women 20, 45, 52, 68, 77, 79, 85, 87, 92, 96, 108, 129, 135, 136, 164, 168, 169, 170, 191, 192, 193, 214.
words 170.
words of Allah 104, 157, 158, 169, 171, 175, 184, 210.
work 200.
worms 44, 50, 55, 66, 73, 193.
wormwood 38.
worry 25, 195.
worship 173.
wounds 39, 55, 88, 126, 154, 156, 168, 192.
wrists 195, 196.
writing 148, 168, 169, 170, 175, 176, 206.